NORTHERN CALIFORNIA TRIVIA

NORTHERN CALIFORNIA TRIVIA

COMPILED BY ERNIE & JILL COUCH

Rutledge Hill Press

513 THIRD AVE., S.   NASHVILLE, TENNESSEE 37210

Published by Rutledge Hill Press, Inc., 513 Third Avenue South, Nashville, Tennessee 37210

Typography by Bailey Typography, Inc.
Cover photograph by Doug Brachey Photography
Color separation by Manning Camera Graphics
Book and cover design by Ernie Couch / Consultx
Special thanks to Teri Mitchell

Library of Congress Cataloging-in-Publication Data
Couch, Ernie, 1949-
    Northern California trivia / compiled by Ernie & Jill Couch.
        p.   cm.
    ISBN 1-55853-040-1
    1. California, Northern—Miscellanea.   2. Questions and answers.
I. Couch, Jill, 1948-   II. Title.
F867.5.C68   1989   89-29823
979.4—dc20   CIP

Printed in the United States of America
1 2 3 4 5 6 7 8 — 94 93 92 91 90 89

PREFACE

Throughout our nation's history, Northern California has often stood in the forefront in development, ingenuity, and leadership. Northern California is comprised of a richly diversified land and people with colorful traditions and a compelling history. Captured within these pages are some of the highlights of this rich heritage, both the known and the not-so-well-known.

Northern California Trivia is designed to be informative, educational, and entertaining. We hope that reading it will motivate you to learn about this great region.

—Ernie & Jill Couch

To
Walter S. Hern, III
and
the great people of Northern California

TABLE OF CONTENTS

GEOGRAPHY

C H A P T E R   O N E

Q. James Savage and his five Indian wives settled what California community?

A. Savage Diggings (Big Oak Flat).

◆

Q. By what other name is "Bayview High School" known?

A. San Quentin.

◆

Q. What city is situated in the exact center of California?

A. Madera.

◆

Q. Eastport, Maine, native James T. Rogers instigated the name of what California coastal town?

A. Westport.

◆

Q. What California town is called the "Cedar Pencil Capital"?

A. Pioneer.

Q. Because it also survived the 1906 earthquake, what town is called "Little San Francisco"?

A. Petaluma.

———◆———

Q. What road once linked all the Spanish settlements of California?

A. El Camino Real (The Royal Road).

———◆———

Q. Where is the longest covered bridge in the United States?

A. Penn Valley.

———◆———

Q. Santa Clara is in the center of what high technology region?

A. The "Silicon Valley."

———◆———

Q. What is the smallest incorporated city in California?

A. Amador City.

———◆———

Q. Where did the ill-fated Donner party encamp?

A. Near Tuckee.

———◆———

Q. What town is dubbed the "Cradle of California"?

A. Sonoma.

Q. What is the name of the 50,000-acre site that is home to nine different tribes of native Americans?

A. Round Valley.

———◆———

Q. What California community has a Miwok Indian Round-house?

A. Ahwahnee.

———◆———

Q. What is the least densely populated county in California?

A. Alpine.

———◆———

Q. Where can the "Old Log Jail" be seen?

A. Markleeville.

———◆———

Q. What city claims the title "Gateway to Yosemite"?

A. Merced.

———◆———

Q. Where did Col. John C. Fremont headquarter his land grant of 44,000 acres?

A. Bear Valley.

———◆———

Q. What city was called "Queen of the Southern Mines" in Mother Lode country?

A. Sonora.

Q. What tiny hamlet was originally named Poison Camp?

A. Zenia.

Q. Where is California's largest inland port?

A. Stockton.

Q. What San Francisco area is known as "Postcard Row"?

A. Alamo Square.

Q. Where does the Alaskan Highway start?

A. I-5 and Highway 97 in Weed.

Q. What Mendocino County town was named for a famous Mexican War general?

A. Fort Bragg (for Gen. Braxton Bragg).

Q. Who was largely responsible for laying out and naming San Francisco's streets?

A. Jasper O'Farrell.

Q. What is the oldest structure on a college campus in the western United States?

A. The mission at the University of Santa Clara.

Q. What town was formerly known as Hardscrabble?

A. Centerville.

———◆———

Q. Malakoff Diggins State Historic Park contains some original buildings from what extinct community?

A. North Bloomfield.

———◆———

Q. The light from the Point Arena lighthouse can be seen how far out at sea?

A. 24 miles.

———◆———

Q. What is the county seat of America's most renowned wine grape growing district?

A. Napa.

———◆———

Q. What town is the gateway to Bigfoot Country?

A. Willow Creek.

———◆———

Q. Where did the Mount Tamalpais Scenic Railroad operate from 1896 to 1931?

A. Mill Valley.

———◆———

Q. What community was formerly called Beals Landing?

A. Westport.

Q. What three northern California counties share borders with Oregon?

A. Del Norte, Siskiyou, and Modoc.

———◆———

Q. What was Marin County's first city?

A. San Rafael.

———◆———

Q. What Mariposa County community was named for the United States of North America?

A. Usona.

———◆———

Q. An 1870s coal boom brought about the naming of what two Ione Valley communities?

A. Carbondale and Lignite.

———◆———

Q. What Mendocino County town's name evolved from the Pomo Indian word *Yosol*?

A. Usal.

———◆———

Q. The community of Willow Ranch is situated on the shore of what large northern California lake?

A. Goose Lake.

———◆———

Q. What community developed in Santa Cruz County around a resort that was founded in 1876 by F. A. Hihn?

A. Capitola.

Q. What was the former name of North Bloomfield?

A. Humbug.

———◆———

Q. Where is the beginning of the famed Seventeen-Mile Drive?

A. Pacific Grove.

———◆———

Q. What three-block-long town is known as the "Gateway to the Mendocino Wine Country"?

A. Hopland.

———◆———

Q. Prior to San Francisco and Los Angeles, where did the Reverend Jim Jones lead his followers?

A. Ukiah (then Redwood Valley).

———◆———

Q. Corte Madera is famous for one of the mills that supplied lumber to build what San Francisco landmark?

A. The Presidio.

———◆———

Q. What city is called "The Jewel of the Bay"?

A. Village of Tiburon.

———◆———

Q. What town was once known as Dorris Bridge?

A. Alturas.

Q. In 1919 what community, first called McAlpine, grew up around the Davies-Johnson Lumber Company in Sierra County?

A. Calpine.

---◆---

Q. Where is the castle that William Randolph Hearst built?

A. San Simeon.

---◆---

Q. What is the Sierra Nevada area known as?

A. "The Mother Lode Country."

---◆---

Q. In what area do homes perch on cliffs 800 feet above the sea?

A. Big Sur.

---◆---

Q. Where is California's largest concentration of Chinese?

A. San Francisco.

---◆---

Q. How many miles long is the famed drive around the Monterey Peninsula?

A. 17.

---◆---

Q. Where is the oldest standing capitol building in California?

A. Benicia.

Q. What state park encompasses a 170-building ghost town?

A. Bodie State Historic Park.

———◆———

Q. Where did Cherokee Indians migrate in order to work in the gold mines?

A. Oroville.

———◆———

Q. For more than a century, what town was the head of navigation on the Sacramento River?

A. Red Bluff.

———◆———

Q. What is the oldest Taoist temple in continuous use in the Western Hemisphere?

A. The Joss House, Weaverville.

———◆———

Q. By what name was Monterey Bay formerly called?

A. San Pedro Bay.

———◆———

Q. What is the "Valley of Green Gold"?

A. Salinas Valley.

———◆———

Q. Where is the oldest government building in California?

A. Monterey (the Custom House).

Q. Where is the Los Cochas adobe?

A. Soledad.

———◆———

Q. Fiddletown was named by settlers from what state?

A. Missouri.

———◆———

Q. What group of 6 small rocky islands lie 28 miles west of San Francisco Bay?

A. The Farallones.

———◆———

Q. By what name was Point Reyes known in 1542?

A. Caler de los Reyes.

———◆———

Q. The town of Likely is in what valley?

A. South Fork.

———◆———

Q. A central location in Kings River Valley led to what community's name?

A. Centerville.

———◆———

Q. What area was known as the "web-foot" settlement?

A. Goose Lake Valley.

Q. What San Benito Spanish place-name means "three pines"?

A. Tres Pinos.

———◆———

Q. Where was Fort Bidwell situated?

A. Surprise Valley.

———◆———

Q. What is the largest lake in Lake County?

A. Clear Lake.

———◆———

Q. The Yuba County town of Marysville was first known by what name?

A. New Mecklenburg.

———◆———

Q. What Fresno County town was formerly known by such names as Kings River Switch, Drapersville, and Wheatville?

A. Kingsburg.

———◆———

Q. Garrote and First Garrote were former names of what Tuolumne County community?

A. Groveland.

———◆———

Q. The Siskiyou County settlement of Klamath River was first known by what name?

A. Honolulu.

Q. In what border town is the post office in Oregon while all elementary students (even those from Oregon) attend school in California?

A. New Pine Creek.

Q. Where is New Brighton Beach?

A. Near Santa Cruz.

Q. For whom was Carson Pass named?

A. Kit Carson.

Q. Where was the first California terminal for the transcontinental railroad?

A. Central Pacific Passenger Station, Sacramento.

Q. What does the name *Alturas* mean?

A. "A valley on top of a mountain."

Q. Who was the Haight of Haight-Asbury?

A. Governor Henry Huntley Haight.

Q. What county did Indians call "The Smiles of God"?

A. Modoc.

Q. What area was named by pioneers who, thinking they were near the Pacific Ocean, stopped to dance and were massacred?

A. Fandango Pass.

◆

Q. What is the westernmost point of the San Francisco peninsula?

A. Point Lobos.

◆

Q. Where was Patty Hearst living when her kidnapping saga began?

A. Berkeley.

◆

Q. Russian Gulch is situated two miles north of what community?

A. Mendocino.

◆

Q. Where is the Marshall Gold Discovery Area?

A. Near Placerville.

◆

Q. Funeral notices are still posted on a lightpole in what California town?

A. Fort Bragg (at Franklin Street and Redwood Avenue).

◆

Q. Who settled Ferndale?

A. Seth and Steven Shaw.

Q. What California place-name is Spanish for "Holy Sacrament"?

A. Sacramento.

———◆———

Q. Where is the headquarters of the Sixth Army?

A. The Presidio.

———◆———

Q. What entire town has been named a State Historical Landmark for its well-preserved Victorian buildings and homes?

A. Ferndale.

———◆———

Q. After several "necktie parties," what community became known as "Hangtown"?

A. Placerville.

———◆———

Q. What present-day town was named in honor of President Zachary Taylor?

A. Rough and Ready.

———◆———

Q. Poverty Flat was the original name of what Shasta County town?

A. Redding.

———◆———

Q. The Hoopa Valley Indian Reservation is in what county?

A. Humboldt.

Q. Where is the oldest standing railroad station west of the Mississippi River?

A. Folsom (the Ashland Freight Depot).

◆

Q. What two areas make up Cambria?

A. East and West Villages.

◆

Q. What is the seat of Nevada County?

A. Nevada City.

◆

Q. First called Smith's Landing, what Contra Costa County town has the name of a biblical city in Syria?

A. Antioch.

◆

Q. What two mountain ridges guard Los Gatos?

A. El Sombroso and El Sereno.

◆

Q. From what county was Congressman Leo Ryan elected?

A. San Mateo.

◆

Q. What town was formerly called Logtown?

A. Mariposa.

Q. What community got its name from the Carmelite friars who accompanied the Spanish settlers?

A. Carmel.

Q. Coaling Station A of the Southern Pacific Railroad led to what town's name?

A. Coalinga.

Q. What protects Crescent City from strong winds?

A. Point St. George.

Q. What street is called "Wall Street of the West"?

A. Montgomery Street, San Francisco.

Q. Where is Atascadero Beach?

A. Morro Bay.

Q. What present-day community had the colorful early nickname of "By Hell"?

A. Woodland.

Q. Chasing a band of Indian raiders led Major James D. Savage to discover what valley?

A. Yosemite.

Q. A shoot-out in 1871 between escapees of the Nevada State Penitentiary and a posse gave what Mono County lake its name?

A. Convict Lake.

Q. Where is the Mission San Antonio De Padua?

A. Near King City.

Q. What Plumas County town was named for an early lumberman who organized the Grizzly Creek Ice Company?

A. Gulling (for Charles Gulling).

Q. In what county are the communities of Ono and Igo?

A. Shasta.

Q. Robert Bousefield named what Contra Costa County community in 1911?

A. Kensington Park.

Q. For whom was Monterey named?

A. Count of Monte-Rey, Viceroy of Mexico.

Q. A large influx of Irish settlers gave what nickname to San Ramon?

A. "Limerick."

Q. What Fresno County town was named for a pioneer lumberman and cattleman from the Pine Ridge and Tollhouse area?

A. Humphreys (for John W. Humphreys).

———◆———

Q. What nickname does Lombard Street in San Francisco have?

A. "Crookedest Street in the World."

———◆———

Q. Where is Benbow Lake?

A. Near Garberville.

———◆———

Q. What town was once known as Campo Seco?

A. San Andreas.

———◆———

Q. Where is the Marin County Civic Center?

A. San Rafael.

———◆———

Q. What cities did "El Camino Real" connect?

A. San Francisco and San Diego.

———◆———

Q. What are the three highest hills in San Francisco?

A. Telegraph, Russian, and Nob.

Q. What town sits in the valley once known as Valley of the Curses of the Soldiers?

A. San Gregorio.

---◆---

Q. Villa Montalvo, home of the late Senator James D. Phelan, is in what community?

A. Saratoga.

---◆---

Q. What does Pescadero mean?

A. "Fishing place."

---◆---

Q. How long is the deepwater channel connecting Stockton to San Francisco Bay?

A. 78 miles.

---◆---

Q. In terms of size, where does California rank in relation to the other 49 states?

A. Third (156,299 square miles).

---◆---

Q. Where did President Warren G. Harding die?

A. The Palace Hotel, San Francisco.

---◆---

Q. What Spanish name did Twin Peaks once have?

A. Los Pechos de la Choca ("the breasts of the Indian maiden").

Q. What nickname was given to Alcatraz?

A. "The Rock."

Q. Who plotted the town of Pittsburg?

A. William Tecumseh Sherman.

Q. What town was once called Doughtery's Station?

A. Dublin.

Q. On what river was the first electric power plant in central California constructed?

A. American (Folsom prison).

Q. What town once called itself the "Cherry City of California"?

A. San Leandro.

Q. Where is Horsetail Falls?

A. Desolation Valley.

Q. A local shingle mill led to what community's name?

A. Shingle Springs.

Q. What is the capital of California?

A. Sacramento.

———◆———

Q. Colored sand and gravel cliffs led to the naming of what Tehama County town?

A. Red Bluff.

———◆———

Q. Because early migrants believed California soil was too sterile, what bountiful valley was considered a dessert?

A. The San Joaquin Valley.

———◆———

Q. Snakehouse Creek is in what county?

A. Mendocino.

———◆———

Q. What town received its name in honor of William C. Ralston, who modestly declined to have a Stanislaus County town named in his honor?

A. Modesto.

———◆———

Q. By what name was San Francisco originally known?

A. Yerba Buena.

———◆———

Q. Northcrest is situated on the southern shore of what lake?

A. Lake Earl.

Q. What is the longest island in the Bay area?

A. Angel Island.

———✦———

Q. Who lived out his later years as the "Lord of Livermore"?

A. Christopher Augustine Buckley.

———✦———

Q. Where is the Pony Express Monument?

A. Meyers.

———✦———

Q. Where was the site of the first Chatauqua in the west?

A. Pacific Grove.

———✦———

Q. What does the name Tassajara mean?

A. "Meat-curing place."

———✦———

Q. What town was laid out on a portion of the Rancho Bolsa Nueva del Cojo in 1864?

A. Castroville.

———✦———

Q. Where was Governor Jerry Brown born?

A. San Francisco.

Q. What community is the seat of Del Norte County?

A. Crescent City.

Q. Freedom was known originally by what name?

A. Whiskey Hill.

Q. Apart from forts and missions, what was California's first town?

A. San Jose.

Q. What is called the "Gibraltar of the Pacific"?

A. Mono rock.

Q. What was the former name of Loleta?

A. Swauger.

Q. For what county did Crescent City serve as the first county seat?

A. Klamath.

Q. Until 1850, Shasta was known by what name?

A. Reading Spring.

Q. Uncle Sam Mountain is situated in what Monterey County mountain range?

A. Santa Lucia.

———◆———

Q. Weed is in what county?

A. Siskiyou.

———◆———

Q. By what two names has Fortuna been known?

A. Springville and Slide.

———◆———

Q. Due to large local chalk deposits, what community was formerly called Chalk Ford?

A. Bieber.

———◆———

Q. Whose shout when he first saw it gave Eureka its name?

A. James Ryan.

———◆———

Q. Shaste Butte City became what present-day town?

A. Yreka.

———◆———

Q. The community of Day is situated in the southwest corner of what county?

A. Modoc.

Q. What community was named for an Indian chief whose name means "Shell-Bearer"?

A. Calpella.

◆

Q. What Sonoma County creek was named for the mail carrier between San Rafael and Sonoma during the Mexican War?

A. Carriger (for Nicholas Carriger).

◆

Q. Herbert Hoover was born in what California community?

A. Palo Alto.

◆

Q. The Round Valley Indian Reservation is situated just north of what community?

A. Covelo.

◆

Q. By what other name is Kelseyville known?

A. Peartown.

◆

Q. Who founded Sonoma?

A. Mariano Vallejo.

◆

Q. What two counties have mountains with the place-name of Two Teats?

A. Madera and Mono.

Q. What was the original name of Saratoga?

A. McCarthysville.

———◆———

Q. Where did the dairy town of Manteca get its name?

A. The Spanish word for butter.

———◆———

Q. What was Knight's Ferry once temporarily renamed?

A. Dentville.

———◆———

Q. Where did the bandit Tiburcio Vasquez commit his last robbery?

A. Paicines.

———◆———

Q. What community did Joaquin Miller describe as "a sort of Hades"?

A. Humbug City.

———◆———

Q. What community lies halfway between Lower Lake and Calistoga?

A. Middletown.

———◆———

Q. By what name was Lakeport once known?

A. Forbestown.

Q. What town was once called Soda Bar for its mineral springs?

A. Paxton.

Q. Where is the home of Travis Air Force Base?

A. Fairfield.

Q. What does Requa's name mean?

A. "Mouth of the river."

Q. Who laid out the town of Madera in 1876?

A. California Lumber Company.

Q. What was Red Bluff's former name?

A. Leodocia.

Q. Mountaineers who were loyal to the Union during the Civil War led to the name of what town?

A. Loyalton.

Q. What Bay area city was incorporated on January 24, 1956?

A. Fremont.

Q. What town was called Rough and Ready when founded in 1874?

A. Etna.

—————◆—————

Q. The ancient name for Britain is applied to what Mendocino County community?

A. Albion.

—————◆—————

Q. Where is the oldest county courthouse in continuous use west of the Mississippi?

A. Mariposa.

—————◆—————

Q. What comunity's name means "little ovens"?

A. Hornitos.

—————◆—————

Q. Boonville in Mendocino County was founded under what name in 1864?

A. Kendall's City.

—————◆—————

Q. What Solano County town was built on land donated by Clipper ship captain Robert H. Waterman?

A. Fairfield.

—————◆—————

Q. John Marsh, who owned Rancho Los Meganos, named what town for his ancestral home in England?

A. Brentwood (for Brentwood in Essex).

Q. What town was once known as Mud Springs?

A. El Dorado.

———◆———

Q. In what California town did famed meatpacker Phillip D. Armour run a butcher shop?

A. Placerville.

———◆———

Q. What town belied its name with 26 saloons?

A. Drytown.

———◆———

Q. Who started the foundations of his fortune in Sheep Ranch?

A. George Hearst.

———◆———

Q. Where was the location of the richest gold diggings in the whole Mother Lode?

A. Carson Hill.

———◆———

Q. What town was once known as Slumgullion?

A. Melones.

———◆———

Q. What California town was named after the brand of the stove that heated a local general store?

A. Clio.

Q. What settlement was the forerunner of Nevada City?

A. Bear Creek Diggings.

◆

Q. A miner found panning gold clad only in his shirt led to the naming of what canyon?

A. Shirt Tail Canyon.

◆

Q. What community was once called Toadtown due to the toads that covered the area during a heavy rainstorm?

A. Johnstonville.

◆

Q. By what two former names was Planada previously known?

A. Geneva and Whitton.

◆

Q. What is the largest of the "delta" islands of the Sacramento River?

A. Grand Island.

◆

Q. Where was the first Episcopal cathedral in Northern California erected in 1860?

A. Benicia.

◆

Q. What town was incorporated in 1908 as Ocean View?

A. Albany.

Q. What town is home to the largest fishing fleet north of San Francisco?

A. Eureka.

------◆------

Q. Where were the seven survivors of Donner Party's "Forlorn Hope" group taken?

A. To a ranch at Wheatland.

------◆------

Q. What town was once known as both Alden Grove and Illinoistown?

A. Colfax.

------◆------

Q. Nearby granite quarries led to what community's name?
A. Rocklin.

------◆------

Q. What city is home to the Placer County Museum?
A. Auburn.

------◆------

Q. In what state park is there a monument to James A. Garfield?

A. Bodie State Historic Park.

------◆------

Q. Where is the Coast Guard Training Center for the West Coast?

A. Alameda.

Q. What was the former name of Georgetown?

A. Growlersburg.

———◆———

Q. Where is the only remaining authentic Chinese temple in northern California?

A. Mendocino (Temple of Kwan Tia).

———◆———

Q. What California town was once known as Ravine City?

A. Placerville.

———◆———

Q. Where is the home of the 7th Infantry Division?

A. Fort Ord.

———◆———

Q. What street in San Francisco is called "Street of 25,000 Lanterns"?

A. Grant Avenue in Chinatown.

———◆———

Q. "High Tech Capital of the World" is the title of what California city?

A. Santa Clara.

———◆———

Q. Where is the Sharpsteen Museum situated?

A. Calistoga.

Q. What is the length (north to south) of California?

A. About 800 miles.

———◆———

Q. Including tidal estuaries, what is the length of the California coast line?

A. About 3,400 miles.

———◆———

Q. McClellan and Mather Air Force bases are near what large California city?

A. Sacramento.

———◆———

Q. Where are the Christian Brothers Wine and Champagne Cellars?

A. St. Helena.

———◆———

Q. What California city has been called "Baghdad by the Bay"?

A. San Francisco.

———◆———

Q. What does the name Palo Alto mean?

A. "Tall Tree."

———◆———

Q. Where is the Bok Kai (Bomb Day) Festival held?

A. Marysville.

Q. In terms of land area, what is the smallest county in northern California?

A. San Francisco.

———◆———

Q. The town of Smith River sits on what waterway?

A. Rowdy Creek.

———◆———

Q. Berkeley was founded on land that was once a part of what Spanish land grant?

A. Peralta Rancho San Antonio.

———◆———

Q. An Indian name from Michigan was applied to what Medera County community in 1908?

A. Nipinnawasee.

———◆———

Q. The Yolo County railroad station that developed into Esparto was known by what name?

A. Esperanza.

———◆———

Q. What military facility is situated in both Yuba County and Nevada County?

A. Beale Air Force Base.

———◆———

Q. Where is the only high school in west Marin County situated?

A. Tomales.

ENTERTAINMENT

C H A P T E R   T W O

Q. Clint Eastwood was mayor of what seaside town in California?

A. Carmel.

———◆———

Q. What was the setting of the television western series, "The Big Valley"?

A. San Joaquin Valley.

———◆———

Q. Charlie Chaplin filmed *The Tramp* in what Fremont district?

A. Niles.

———◆———

Q. What is Danny Glover's birthplace?

A. San Francisco.

———◆———

Q. What California city had a TV miniseries spoof of soap operas named after it?

A. Fresno.

Q. Lola Montez, famous courtesan and dancer, owned her home in what community?

A. Grass Valley.

◆

Q. What NBC comedy-drama series dealt with a widow and her children who relocated to Lake Tahoe?

A. "Shirley."

◆

Q. In what town was actor Tom Hanks born?
A. Oakland.

◆

Q. The oldest continuously operating theater west of the Rockies is situated in what California town?

A. Nevada City.

◆

Q. Where in the Sierra Nevada mountains is an operating steam engine train?

A. At the Yosemite Mountain-Sugar Pine Railroad.

◆

Q. What early-1950s television series set in San Francisco's Sea Cliff area was the first NBC show to use rear-screen projection?

A. "One Man's Family."

◆

Q. The movie *High Noon* was filmed in what California town?
A. Railtown.

Q. Where was singer-songwriter Malvina Reynolds born in 1901?

A. Berkeley.

Q. In what town did Fatty Arbuckle's weekend escapades bring his career to an end?

A. San Francisco.

Q. The film *American Graffiti* was based on George Lucas's boyhood in what city?

A. Modesto.

Q. What was the birthplace of Mel Blanc?

A. San Francisco.

Q. Who was the first California Artichoke Queen?

A. Marilyn Monroe, 1947.

Q. Where is the only existing former Spanish gambling casino in California?

A. Chapete's Place in Portola Valley (now known as Alpine Beer Garden).

Q. Who popularized the song "Do you know the Way to San Jose?"

A. Dionne Warwick.

Q. What El Cerrito area band preceded Creedence Clearwater Revival?

A. Tommy Fogerty and the Blue Velvets.

◆

Q. At what San Francisco station did "P.M. Magazine" originate in 1976, under the name, "Evening Magazine"?

A. KPIX-TV.

◆

Q. Where was George Lucas born?

A. Modesto.

◆

Q. What half-hour western set in San Francisco during the 1850s aired on national television from 1957 to 1959?

A. "The Californians."

◆

Q. Northern California-born actor Mike Conners played agent Ben Slater in what 1981-82 television show?

A. "Today's F.B.I."

◆

Q. Where in Oakland is the world's first three-dimensional theme park?

A. Children's Fairyland.

◆

Q. What San Francisco tourist attraction is home to seafood restaurants and the fishing fleet?

A. Fisherman's Wharf.

Q. Where was Mary Pickford's *Rebecca of Sunnybrook Farm* filmed?

A. Pleasanton.

◆

Q. Where was the world's only chicken pharmacy?

A. Petaluma.

◆

Q. In 1988 the inaugural Tuolumne County Wild West Film Fest was dedicated to the memory of what cowboy actor?

A. Slim Pickens.

◆

Q. Where was Barry Bostwick born?

A. San Mateo.

◆

Q. Where is the Dai Loy Gambling House Museum?

A. Locke.

◆

Q. What famous shopping area was once a chocolate factory?

A. Ghiradelli Square.

◆

Q. What infamous former federal prison can now be visited by boat tour?

A. Alcatraz.

Q. Pat Morita was what town's native son?

A. Berkeley.

◆

Q. Where is the home of the Grand National and Junior Grand National Livestock Exhibition?

A. The Cow Palace, Daly City.

◆

Q. The television comedy-drama "Eight Is Enough" was set in what northern California city?

A. Sacramento.

◆

Q. In what California city did the first topless dancer in the United States appear?

A. San Francisco.

◆

Q. When was Ronald Reagan first elected governor of California?

A. 1966.

◆

Q. What character did Karl Malden play in the television series, "The Streets of San Francisco"?

A. Detective Lieutenant Mike Stone.

◆

Q. Where is Amy Irving's birthplace?

A. Palo Alto.

Q. What "Little House on the Prairie" actress was born in Berkeley?

A. Melissa Sue Anderson.

———————◆———————

Q. What northern California-born rock and roller received *Billboard* magazine's 1955 Triple Award for his single "Maybellene"?

A. Chuck Berry.

———————◆———————

Q. Where is the real Carrington "Dynasty" mansion?

A. Filoli House and Gardens, Woodside.

———————◆———————

Q. Where was "Incredible Hulk" star Bill Bixby born?

A. San Francisco.

———————◆———————

Q. In 1982 the name of what northern California television series became the label for two wines?

A. "Falcon Crest."

———————◆———————

Q. In 1975 what became the Doobie Brothers' first number one hit single?

A. "Black Water."

———————◆———————

Q. What flamboyant San Francisco attorney once represented topless waitresses in a lawsuit?

A. Melvin Belli.

Q. Where was Clint Eastwood born?

A. San Francisco.

———◆———

Q. What Oakland-made film on explorers was the first movie released by Hollywood?

A. *Big Game Hunting in Africa.*

———◆———

Q. Where was the world's largest "Outdoor Rummy Game" staged?

A. Portuguese Square, Ripon.

———◆———

Q. What bizarre exhibit toured California in the late 1800s as proof of two bandits' deaths?

A. The head of Joaquin Murrieta and the hand of Three-Fingered Jack.

———◆———

Q. What was Lola Montez's real name?

A. Maria Delores Porris Gilbert.

———◆———

Q. Who was Lola Montez's protégée?

A. Lotta Crabtree.

———◆———

Q. Where was singer/actress Julie London born?

A. Santa Rosa.

Q. Who brought fame to the town of Murphys when he made a film there in 1934?

A. Will Rogers.

———◆———

Q. What Maestro ruled the San Francisco Opera for 25 years?

A. Kurt Herbert Adler.

———◆———

Q. Who was one of the most infamous graduates of Santa Clara High School in San Jose?

A. Fatty Arbuckle.

———◆———

Q. Lasting only one month in 1981, what dramatic series starring Tom and Dick Smothers was set at KSFB-TV in San Francisco?

A. "Fitz and Bones."

———◆———

Q. What star of "I Spy" was born in Oakland?

A. Robert Culp.

———◆———

Q. What major event occurs in Alturas in early July?

A. Fandango Celebration.

———◆———

Q. When is the annual Monterey Jazz Festival held?

A. Third weekend in September.

Q. The Barkley ranch of "The Big Valley" supposedly covered how many acres?

A. 30,000.

◆

Q. Where is Johnny Mathis' birthplace?

A. San Francisco.

◆

Q. Where is the Great Bed Race held each year?

A. Napa.

◆

Q. What granddaughter of William Randolph Hearst made the cover of *People* magazine when her first child was born?

A. Patty Hearst.

◆

Q. Where is the child-sized Children's Fairyland?

A. Oakland.

◆

Q. Where are the fabulous Feather Fiesta Days held?

A. Oroville.

◆

Q. What star of "Sea Hunt" and *Airplane* was born in San Leandro?

A. Lloyd Bridges.

Q. Lantern-lit processions herald what event in Pacific Grove?

A. Feast of Lanterns.

———◆———

Q. Where is Wagon Train Week held?

A. Placerville.

———◆———

Q. What 1974 hit won the Pointer Sisters a Grammy?

A. "Fairy Tale."

———◆———

Q. Where is the Napa Valley Wine Auction held?

A. St. Helena.

———◆———

Q. Where is the real setting for "Falcon Crest"?

A. Spring Mountain Vineyards, St. Helena.

———◆———

Q. Where was "Hill Street Blues" Charles Haid born?

A. San Francisco.

———◆———

Q. In the television western "Barbary Coast," Doug Mc-Clure played Cash Conover, owner of what San Francisco gaming house?

A. Golden Gate Casino.

Q. Where is Keith Carradine's hometown?

A. San Mateo.

———◆———

Q. In 1969 what single went to number one for Sly and the Family Stone?

A. "Everyday People."

———◆———

Q. Where did Rod McKuen get his start?

A. The Purple Onion, San Francisco.

———◆———

Q. Where did jazz singer Carol Ann Leigh attend college in 1956 and 1957?

A. San Jose State University.

———◆———

Q. Janis Joplin settled in what California city in 1966?

A. San Francisco.

———◆———

Q. What Bay area group became known for such bizarre songs as "Quay Lude" and "Dr. Strangekiss"?

A. The Tubes.

———◆———

Q. What was the birthplace of Ronnie Schell?

A. Richmond.

Q. Barry Bostwick played bumbling Sergeant Tucker Pendleton of the San Francisco Police Department in what 1981 light crime show?

A. "Foul Play."

———◆———

Q. Where is Farley Granger's hometown?

A. San Jose.

———◆———

Q. What northern California railroad's rolling stock was featured in the 1963-70 television series "Petticoat Junction"?

A. Sierra Railway Company.

———◆———

Q. What singer was a longtime companion of Governor Jerry Brown?

A. Linda Ronstadt.

———◆———

Q. Where is the Russian River Jazz Festival held?

A. Guerneville.

———◆———

Q. What television medical drama starring Pernell Roberts was set in San Francisco Memorial Hospital"?

A. "Trapper John, M.D."

———◆———

Q. Where was rock and roller Chuck Berry born on January 15, 1926?

A. San Jose.

Q. Where were the Pointer Sisters born?

A. Oakland.

◆

Q. What TV series helped make Karl Malden and Michael Douglas famous?

A. "The Streets of San Francisco."

◆

Q. Who founded the San Francisco Opera?

A. Gaetano Merola.

◆

Q. Who became the richest Hollywood star of her time thanks to her relationship with William Randolph Hearst?

A. Marion Davies.

◆

Q. Where was Jeffrey Tambor born?

A. San Francisco.

◆

Q. In the 1950s "Four Star Playhouse," Dick Powell played several episodes as the owner of what San Francisco night spot?

A. Dante's Inferno.

◆

Q. What famed Hollywood designer earned an M.A. in French from Stanford?

A. Edith Head.

Q. What dance did Lola Montez make famous?

A. The Spider Dance.

———◆———

Q. Whose volunteer drug experiments at Stanford led to the movie *One Flew Over the Cuckoo's Nest?*

A. Ken Kesey.

———◆———

Q. What Stanford University students became the top-selling music group in 1960?

A. The Kingston Trio.

———◆———

Q. What was Mills Watson's birthplace?

A. Oakland.

———◆———

Q. In the hit western series, "Have Gun Will Travel," Paladin, played by Richard Boone, was based out of what location?

A. Hotel Carlton, San Francisco.

———◆———

Q. What northern California native wrote the screenplay for *San Francisco?*

A. Anita Loos.

———◆———

Q. Where was Bradford Dillman born?

A. San Francisco.

Q. In 1865 who made her name in Byron's *Mazeppa* at the San Francisco Opera House by riding strapped to the back of a horse while wearing flesh-colored tights?

A. Adah Theodore Isaccs Menken.

◆

Q. The Doobie Brothers band was formed from the remnants of what previous group?

A. Pud.

◆

Q. What is The Wooz?

A. The first redwood labyrinth amusement park, Vacaville.

◆

Q. What "Three's Company" star's hometown is San Bruno?

A. Suzanne Somers.

◆

Q. What former Miss California and Broadway actress was Eugene O'Neill's third wife?

A. Carlotta Monterey (formerly Hazel Tharsing of Oakland).

◆

Q. What governor refused to live in the governor's mansion and persuaded backers to buy him a million-dollar villa?

A. Ronald Reagan.

◆

Q. What rank in the San Francisco Police Department did Robert T. Ironside hold in the series "Ironside"?

A. Chief of Detectives.

Q. What songwriter was denied her diploma from San Francisco's Lowell High School because her parents were pacifists?

A. Malvina Reynolds.

Q. "Believe It Or Not," what journalist/entrepreneur was born in Santa Rosa?

A. Robert L. Ripley.

Q. What free spirited *San Francisco Examiner* journalist inspired the movie *His Girl Friday?*

A. Adela Rogers St. John.

Q. What 1950s sitcom was built around a Norwegian family living on Steiner Street in San Francisco in 1917?

A. "Mama."

Q. Where is "Mannix" star Mike Conners' hometown?

A. Fresno.

Q. What is the oldest symphony in California?

A. San Jose Symphony.

Q. What famous violinist made his debut at the age of eight with the San Francisco Symphony?

A. Yehudi Menuhin.

Q. What Fresno native won the Pulitzer Prize for his play, *The Time of Your Life?*

A. William Saroyan.

Q. Comedian Mort Sol, noted for his political satire, began his career at what club in San Francisco?

A. The hungry i.

Q. What soprano coloratura sang free in San Francisco to spite Oscar Hammerstein?

A. Luisa Tetrazzini.

Q. Where can $100 million of classic automobiles be viewed?

A. The Bering Museum, Danville.

Q. What was the actual name of Slim Pickens, who spent the last few years of his life in Tuolumne County?

A. Louis Burton Lindley.

Q. What did the *B* in Alice B. Toklas stand for?

A. Babette.

Q. What San Francisco restaurant popularized Polynesian cuisine and exotic drinks?

A. Trader Vic's.

Q. Rock Hudson played Stewart McMillan, Commissioner of Police in San Francisco, in what 1970s television series?

A. "McMillan and Wife."

Q. Who was discovered while swimming in Billy Roses's Aquacade at the San Francisco World's Fair?

A. Esther Williams.

Q. Where was "Different Strokes" star Todd Bridges born?

A. San Francisco.

Q. What was Sally Stanford's real name?

A. Mabel Marcia Busby Goodan Fansler Bayhaam Spagnoli Rapp Gump Kenna.

Q. In the late-1970s, what San Francisco husband and wife mime team had their own half-hour variety show on CBS?

A. Robert Shields and Lorene Yarnell.

Q. As early as 1959, what duo were singing together at San Jose State University?

A. The Smothers Brothers.

Q. Where was Sam Elliot born?

A. Sacramento (August 9, 1944).

Q. Who played the role of Jim Conrad in the television show, "San Francisco International Airport"?

A. Lloyd Bridges.

◆

Q. Who produced the PBS series, "San Francisco Mix"?

A. Richard Moore.

◆

Q. The short-lived television series "Sons and Daughters" was set at Southwest High in what city?

A. Stockton.

◆

Q. On what date did "The Streets of San Francisco" first air on television?

A. September 16, 1972.

◆

Q. Where was Peter Lind Hayes born?

A. San Francisco, 1915.

◆

Q. Where was the setting of the half-hour sitcom, "Too Close for Comfort"?

A. San Francisco.

◆

Q. What San Francisco gay group is known for its members' outrageous antics, fishnet-stockings, and mini-skirted nuns' habits?

A. The Sisters of Perpetual Indulgence.

Q. Where was singer, actor, and composer Rod McKuen born on April 19, 1933?

A. Oakland.

———◆———

Q. In 1963 what northern California-born singer and guitarist wrote the anti-atomic bomb song, "What Have They Done to the Rain"?

A. Malvina Reynolds.

———◆———

Q. Where is the world's only museum of advertising characters?

A. Museum of Modern Mythology, San Francisco.

———◆———

Q. What "All My Children" star was born in Sacramento?

A. James Mitchell.

———◆———

Q. What San Francisco-born blues guitarist composed the theme song for the movie *Mandingo?*

A. Hi Tide Harris.

———◆———

Q. Where was Beverly Garland of "My Three Sons" born?

A. Santa Cruz.

———◆———

Q. In what county was the western *Shadow Riders* shot in 1983?

A. Tuolumne.

Q. In 1919 what became the first motion picture to utilize the Sierra Railroad as a prop?

A. *The Red Glove.*

◆

Q. What 1980 film chronicled the friendship of Jack Kerouac and Neal and Carolyn Cassady?

A. *Heart Beat.*

◆

Q. Where is the World's Largest Teddy Bear?

A. International Toy Museum, San Francisco.

◆

Q. What scenic round-trip steam train excursion goes to Bear Mountain?

A. Roaring Camp and Big Trees Railroad.

◆

Q. What singer was born in and left his heart in San Francisco?

A. Tony Martin.

◆

Q. What filmmaker did Dr. Max Rafferty call "the greatest educator of the century"?

A. Walt Disney.

◆

Q. Each October San Jose hosts what 450-foot-long maze filled with "ghosts and goblins"?

A. World's Largest Haunted House.

Q. Who wrote "Proud Mary"?

A. John Fogerty.

◆

Q. Where was the Doobie Brothers band formed in 1970?

A. San Jose.

◆

Q. Where was Markie Post of "Night Court" born?

A. Palo Alto.

◆

Q. What two singles recorded by Johnny Mathis became number one in 1957?

A. "Chances Are" and "The Twelfth of Never."

◆

Q. What 1960s group cut such great songs as "California Dreamin'" and "San Francisco (Wear Some Flowers in Your Hair)"?

A. The Mamas and the Papas.

◆

Q. What Bay area group formed in 1974 produced such albums as *Paper Money* and *Jump on It?*

A. Montrose.

◆

Q. Where was Karen Valentine born?

A. Santa Rosa.

Q. In what year did Quicksilver Messenger Service release its first album on Capitol?

A. 1968.

◆

Q. What group was the forerunner of Sly and the Family Stone?

A. Stoner.

◆

Q. Where was *Pretty in Pink* star Molly Ringwald born?

A. Rosewood.

◆

Q. What 1935 movie starring Edward G. Robinson was set in San Francisco gold rush days?

A. *Barbary Coast.*

◆

Q. Where can exotic animals be seen in a 160-acre wildlife theme park?

A. Marine World Africa/USA, Vallejo.

◆

Q. Who were the two leading stars in the 1952 movie, *The San Francisco Story?*

A. Joel McCrea and Yvonne De Carlo.

◆

Q. Clark Gable played what character in the 1936 movie *San Francisco?*

A. Blackie Norton.

HISTORY

Q. The re-enactment of the "Celebrated Jumping Frog of Calaveras County" in 1928 celebrated what event?

A. The paving of the streets in Angels Camp.

———◆———

Q. In 1879, who robbed the Roseburg-Redding stage in Hedge Creek Falls?

A. Black Bart.

———◆———

Q. What was the distance between each of the missions the Franciscans founded in California?

A. One day's journey.

———◆———

Q. What was the original name of Dunsmuir?

A. Pusher (for the wood-burning engines that pushed trains over the summit).

———◆———

Q. Who was called the "Father of California"?

A. Mexican General Mariano G. Vallejo.

Q. Where were the first free public schools in California?

A. San Francisco.

───────◆───────

Q. What 1852 lumber port is now famous as an artists'/vacation colony?

A. Mendocino.

───────◆───────

Q. For years, what was the West Coast's most important labor newspaper?

A. *Coast Seaman's Journal.*

───────◆───────

Q. In 1812 Russian seal-fur hunters founded a trading outpost now known as what state historic park?

A. Fort Ross.

───────◆───────

Q. When opened in 1937, what structure was called the "Bridge That Couldn't Be Built"?

A. Golden Gate Bridge.

───────◆───────

Q. When did the University of California become coeducational?

A. 1870.

───────◆───────

Q. What trains were named by loggers who said, "You can smell them before you see them"?

A. The "Skunk" trains.

Q. What was the private language developed from 1880 to 1920?

A. *Boontling* (still used today by *boonters*).

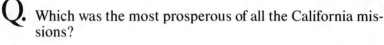

Q. Which was the most prosperous of all the California missions?

A. Mission San Jose.

Q. What historical event occurred at John Sutter's sawmill on January 24, 1848?

A. The discovery of gold, setting off the Gold Rush.

Q. How many miners died in the tragic Argonaut Mine Fire of 1922?

A. 47.

Q. Where was the Bear Flag first raised on June 14, 1846?

A. Sonoma.

Q. What famed Indian fighter fought with John Fremont?

A. Kit Carson.

Q. Why did John ("Snowshoe") Thompson get his nickname?

A. For carrying the mail over the Sierra Nevada on snowshoes when wagons could not cross the passes.

Q. In the 1850s, what did one of the Studebaker brothers sell in Placerville?

A. Wheelbarrows.

———◆———

Q. Where is one of the best collections of World War II aircraft?

A. Castle Air Museum, near Atwater.

———◆———

Q. What notorious bandit staged most of his raids from Hornitos?

A. Joaquin Murrieta.

———◆———

Q. Where were the first Chinese tong wars fought in California?

A. Chinese Camp.

———◆———

Q. What city became the first capital of California on August 16, 1775?

A. Monterey.

———◆———

Q. Where was California's first railroad company organized?

A. Nevada City.

———◆———

Q. Where was former Chief Justice Earl Warren born and raised?

A. Oakland (March 19, 1891).

Q. What California city was once called the "most desperate town in the West"?

A. Pleasanton.

Q. What is California's largest adobe?

A. General Vallejo's rancho (the Old Adobe at Petaluma Adobe State Historic Park).

Q. Who is most often credited with having Yosemite declared a national park?

A. John Muir.

Q. Who was the first and only president of the Bear Flag Republic?

A. William B. Ide.

Q. Who first discovered the gold at Sutter's Mill?

A. James Marshall.

Q. In 1911 who was the last wild tribesman to emerge from the mountain forests?

A. Ishi, a Yahi Yana Indian.

Q. Who dedicated Whiskeytown Dam in 1963?

A. John F. Kennedy.

Q. What was the original name of the Maritime Federation of the Pacific?

A. Wharf and Wave Federation.

———◆———

Q. What 1872-73 war was called the most expensive Indian war ever fought in America?

A. The Modoc War.

———◆———

Q. Who were the *Californios?*

A. A party of progressive Castillians that began in the 1820s.

———◆———

Q. Who was one of the most noted pioneer explorers of California?

A. John C. Fremont.

———◆———

Q. How long did the first Pony Express ride from Sacramento to Placerville take?

A. 2 hours, 59 minutes.

———◆———

Q. Where were one-fifth of all the Liberty war ships built?

A. Richmond.

———◆———

Q. What was the site of the 1939 Golden Gate International Exposition?

A. Treasure Island.

Q. Where did Capt. John Montgomery first raise the American flag claiming California for the United States?

A. Portsmouth Square.

Q. What did "Blood Thursday" in 1934 precipitate in San Francisco?

A. A general strike.

Q. Who founded Santa Clara College?

A. Jesuit fathers.

Q. How much is the pyramid of gold bars at the Old Mint worth?

A. $4 million.

Q. What is the official California state nickname?

A. "The Golden State."

Q. What San Francisco area is all that remains of the Barbary Coast?

A. Jackson Square.

Q. What famous French pirate raided Monterey in 1818?

A. Hypolite Bouchard.

Q. What event celebrated the rebuilding of San Francisco and the opening of the Panama Canal?

A. 1915 Panama-Pacific International Exposition.

———◆———

Q. What is the oldest family assocation in the United States?

A. Kong Chou Temple in Chinatown, San Francisco.

———◆———

Q. What was California's first cathedral?

A. Old St. Mary's Church, San Francisco.

———◆———

Q. When was the world's first cable car put into use?

A. 1873 (in San Francisco).

———◆———

Q. What was California's oldest civil settlement?

A. El Pueblo de San Jose de Guadalupe, founded in 1777.

———◆———

Q. Where was former U.S. Defense Secretary Caspar Weinberger born?

A. San Francisco.

———◆———

Q. Who was California's first governor when it became a state in 1850?

A. Pete Burnett.

Q. What bank became the Bank of America?

A. Bank of Italy.

———◆———

Q. Why was the Pulgas Water Temple constructed?

A. To commemorate the delivery of water from Hetch Hetchy to San Francisco.

———◆———

Q. Why were the presidios established?

A. To protect the missions.

———◆———

Q. What is the oldest structure in San Jose?

A. Peralta Adobe.

———◆———

Q. What famed English explorer beached his ships for repairs on the California coast?

A. Sir Francis Drake, who claimed the land for Queen Elizabeth.

———◆———

Q. When was gold first discovered in the Sierra Mountains?

A. 1848.

———◆———

Q. When did California become a U.S. possession?

A. July 7, 1846.

Q. What is the oldest continuous wine-producing business in California?

A. Paul Masson Vineyards, Saratoga.

———◆———

Q. How did Russian Hill get its name?

A. It was an early burying ground for Russian sailors.

———◆———

Q. By what name was Mission Delores formerly known?

A. San Francisco de Asis.

———◆———

Q. What was first convened in San Jose in 1849?

A. The California legislature.

———◆———

Q. What alleged former madam, author, and restauranteur became mayor of Sausalito in 1976?

A. Sally Stanford.

———◆———

Q. Where did California's labor movement begin?

A. San Francisco.

———◆———

Q. California was the first state to fund special classes for students with what handicaps?

A. Speech impediments.

Q. How many missions did the Franciscans establish in California?

A. 21.

◆

Q. What city was known as the "Breadbasket of the World"?

A. Stockton.

◆

Q. Where was the site of the first West Coast naval station?

A. Mare Island, founded in 1869.

◆

Q. What did John Sutter call his nearly 100,000 acres of land, which included the site of Sacramento?

A. New Helvetia.

◆

Q. What is believed to be the oldest operational firefighting organization in California?

A. Benicia Volunteer Fire Department.

◆

Q. Where is the oldest continuously used post office in California?

A. Auburn.

◆

Q. What were the dairymen's homes in Ferndale known as?

A. "Butterfat Palaces."

Q. Who invented the first cable-drawn street cars?

A. Andrew Halladie, in 1873.

———◆———

Q. Who built the town of Locke?

A. Members of a Chinese tong, about 1915.

———◆———

Q. Where was the first constitution of California written in 1849?

A. Colton Hall, Monterey.

———◆———

Q. What two cities did California's first railroad connect in February 1856?

A. Sacramento and Folsom.

———◆———

Q. What was the first European outpost in the California interior?

A. Sutter's Fort, erected in 1839.

———◆———

Q. Which was the twenty-first and last Franciscan mission established in California?

A. San Francisco Solano.

———◆———

Q. How many times has San Francisco rebuilt itself after fires?

A. Seven.

Q. What was a major contributing factor to Berkeley's growth?

A. The founding of the University of California.

———◆———

Q. When did California experience its "Great Boom"?

A. 1887-88.

———◆———

Q. What British businessman declared himself "Emperor of these United States and protector of Mexico" and "ruled" San Francisco for 21 years?

A. Emperor Norton.

———◆———

Q. How many San Franciscans attended Emperor Norton's funeral in 1880?

A. Over 30,000.

———◆———

Q. Who was the "Birdman of Alcatraz"?

A. Robert Stroud.

———◆———

Q. In what year did a break in the securities market and failure of Jay Cooke and Co. trigger an economic panic?

A. 1873.

———◆———

Q. Where was the first chapter of the United Nations signed?

A. Veterans Memorial Building, San Francisco.

Q. Whom does Coit Memorial Tower honor?

A. San Francisco's volunteer firefighters.

———◆———

Q. What sidewheeler ship was wrecked on Point St. George Reef in 1865?

A. *Brother Jonathan.*

———◆———

Q. As members resorted to cannibalism, how many of the original 89-person Donner Party survived the winter of 1846-47?

A. 45.

———◆———

Q. When was the California state capitol building completed?

A. 1874.

———◆———

Q. What was the first headquarters of the Republican party in California?

A. Golden Eagle Hotel, Sacramento.

———◆———

Q. After the overthrow of Monterey, what was California's new name?

A. Alta California.

———◆———

Q. When was San Francisco founded?

A. 1776.

Q. Where did Al Capone spend eleven years in California?

A. Alcatraz.

———◆———

Q. Who earned fame organizing migrant farm workers in California?

A. Cesar Chavez.

———◆———

Q. Aviator and war hero Jimmy Doolittle was a native of what California town?

A. Alameda.

———◆———

Q. Where was former U.S. Secretary of Defense Robert S. McNamara born?

A. San Francisco.

———◆———

Q. When did Jedadiah Smith lead the first overland expedition from Utah to Mission San Gabriel, California?

A. 1826.

———◆———

Q. Who reached Monterey in January 1846 in his "exploratory" expedition to the West?

A. Captain John Charles Fremont.

———◆———

Q. What 1978 vote cut local property taxes in California in half?

A. Proposition 13.

Q. Who raised the American flag over the Custom House in Monterey on July 7, 1846?

A. Commander John D. Sloat.

———◆———

Q. What is the California state motto?

A. "Eureka" ("I have found [it]"), referring to successful gold seekers.

———◆———

Q. When was the second California state constitution adopted?

A. May 7, 1879.

———◆———

Q. Who were the "Big Four" of the Central Pacific Railroad?

A. Collis P. Huntington, Leland Stanford, Charles Crocker, and Mark Hopkins.

———◆———

Q. Who did Black Bart turn out to be?

A. Charles C. Bolton, a mining engineer.

———◆———

Q. What was San Francisco's first central labor body?

A. San Francisco Trades Union.

———◆———

Q. In the 1934 elections, what did EPIC stand for?

A. End Poverty in California.

Q. What famous ruler visited Spreckel's sugar refinery?

A. The King of the Hawaiian Islands.

---◆---

Q. On what campus did the Free Speech Movement begin in 1964?

A. University of California, Berkeley.

---◆---

Q. What was the name of Sir Francis Drake's treasure-laden ship?

A. *Golden Hinde*.

---◆---

Q. Who bought Fort Ross from the Russians?

A. John Sutter.

---◆---

Q. When was California first colonized?

A. April 1769.

---◆---

Q. Between 1848 and 1852, how much did the California state population increase?

A. From 15,000 to 250,000.

---◆---

Q. What was the purpose of the Alien Land Act of 1913 (the Webb Act)?

A. It restricted Japanese landholdings.

Q. What was the Mother Lode's first newspaper?

A. The *Sonora Herald*.

———————◆———————

Q. When was San Francisco's first Vigilance Committee founded?

A. 1851.

———————◆———————

Q. Where was the first radio broadcast from an airplane?

A. Crissey Field, San Francisco.

———————◆———————

Q. What was the order of admission of California to the United States?

A. 31st.

———————◆———————

Q. What Franciscan friar, called the "patron saint of California," began California's chain of missions in 1768?

A. Junipero Serra.

———————◆———————

Q. How many people died or were ruled missing in the Great Earthquake of 1906?

A. 500.

———————◆———————

Q. By 1909, how many new buildings had been built in San Francisco?

A. 20,000.

Q. Approximately how many Indian reservations are there in California?

A. 32.

----◆----

Q. What railroad was the largest landowner in California in 1919?

A. Southern Pacific.

----◆----

Q. Where is Sutter's Fort preserved?

A. Sacramento.

----◆----

Q. In 1812 who established Fort Ross, a trading post 60 miles north of San Francisco?

A. The Russians.

----◆----

Q. Where is the birthplace of former U.S. Attorney General Edwin Meese?

A. Oakland.

----◆----

Q. When did the Federal Government begin setting land apart as national forests?

A. 1892.

----◆----

Q. When was the California State Department of Agriculture created?

A. 1919.

Q. Where was the first public high school in California?

A. San Francisco.

———◆———

Q. When were the 21 Franciscan missions in California founded?

A. Between 1769 and 1823.

———◆———

Q. Who led the decisive defeat of the Modoc War of 1873?

A. Captain Ben Wright.

———◆———

Q. What bridge built in 1892 spans the San Lorenzo River?

A. The Felton covered bridge.

———◆———

Q. Who is called the founder of San Francisco?

A. Juan Bautista de Anza.

———◆———

Q. By what name was California's first legislative body known in November 1822?

A. The Diputación.

———◆———

Q. When did California become a Territory of the Republic of Mexico?

A. March 26, 1825.

Q. What was the first U.S. ship to dock in Monterey?

A. The *Otter*, in 1796.

Q. When did the first overland immigrant train arrive in California from the Midwest?

A. 1841.

Q. What was Monterey's House of Four Winds named after?

A. The weather vane on top of the house.

Q. Who made the first non-stop flight from San Francisco to Los Angeles?

A. Silas Christofferson, 1914.

Q. Who was known as the "Pathfinder"?

A. John C. Fremont.

Q. From where did Johann August Sutter immigrate?

A. Switzerland.

Q. What was the first group to organize a union in San Francisco in 1850?

A. Printers.

Q. When was Sacramento founded?

A. October 14, 1848.

———◆———

Q. What was the primary consequence of the 1848 Treaty of Guadalupe Hidalgo?

A. Mexico formally relinquished California.

———◆———

Q. Who were the "Hounds"?

A. An 1850s San Francisco gang that attacked minorities.

———◆———

Q. What significant financial event happened on August 27, 1875?

A. The Bank of California crashed.

———◆———

Q. What did rioters burn in San Francisco in 1877?

A. Chinese laundries.

———◆———

Q. What did public normal schools in California become?

A. State teachers' colleges.

———◆———

Q. By what other name was the Sand-Lot Party known?

A. Workingman's Party of California.

Q. What did an 1881 treaty with China regulate?

A. Immigration into the United States.

Q. What organization was formed to protect family-type farms?

A. The California State Grange.

Q. What was the Lincoln-Roosevelt League?

A. A group of liberal Republicans.

Q. Where was the first brick house in California built?

A. Monterey (on Decatur Street).

Q. What July 22, 1916 parade was disrupted by a bombing?

A. San Francisco Preparedness Day parade.

Q. Who was the first white man to settle the interior of California?

A. Johann (John) Sutter.

Q. When was the "great drought"?

A. 1862.

Q. How was Juan Bautista de Anza rewarded for his discovery of Alta California?

A. With the governorship of New Mexico.

———◆———

Q. What was the Independence League?

A. A group of liberal Democrats.

———◆———

Q. When were the Franciscan missions secularized?

A. 1834-37.

———◆———

Q. How much gold was mined in 1852, the year of the industry's largest production?

A. $81,000,000.

———◆———

Q. What was the first one thousand-ton steamer to dock in San Francisco?

A. The *California*.

———◆———

Q. What tragic event happened on February 23, 1855?

A. Black Friday, a gang panic that led to a depression.

———◆———

Q. What was Union Iron Works originally known as?

A. Donahue Brothers Foundry.

Q. What substitute for money was known as a "California bank note"?

A. Animal hides.

———————◆———————

Q. What was the first river steamer to make regular runs from San Francisco to Sacramento?

A. The *Pioneer*.

———————◆———————

Q. What was "Fort Gunnybags"?

A. Vigilante headquarters, 1856.

———————◆———————

Q. What company produced the first stagecoach used in California?

A. Concord Coach.

———————◆———————

Q. What was California's first railroad?

A. Sacramento Valley Line.

———————◆———————

Q. Who organized the Atlantic and Pacific Steamship Line in 1891?

A. San Francisco merchants.

———————◆———————

Q. Who built the San Francisco and San Joaquin Valley Railroad?

A. Merchant Traffic Association.

Q. When was the Northern Pacific railroad line to Eureka completed?

A. 1914.

Q. When did San Francisco get its first street cars?

A. 1861.

Q. What plane made the first round-trip flight from San Francisco to Manila?

A. The *China Clipper*.

Q. What California city was once known as the world's worst "shanghaiing" port?

A. San Francisco.

Q. When was the first newspaper in California printed?

A. 1846.

Q. What was the first effective state federated labor body?

A. The Mechanics' State Council.

Q. Where was the first American school in California?

A. Mission Santa Clara.

Q. What California governor brought the first printing press to Monterey?

A. Jose Figueroa.

———————◆———————

Q. Where did Berkeley get its name?

A. From George Berkeley, Bishop of Cloyne, Ireland.

———————◆———————

Q. Who recognized Monterey as the capital of California in 1775?

A. The King of Spain.

———————◆———————

Q. After the 1906 earthquake, where did 50,000 residents of San Francisco move?

A. Oakland.

———————◆———————

Q. How much money did Sacramento offer for the honor of being the state capital?

A. $1 million.

———————◆———————

Q. When was the San Francisco-Oakland Bay Bridge opened?

A. 1936.

———————◆———————

Q. When did most of the Russian settlers leave California?

A. 1841.

Q. Where did "The Hounds" and "Sydney Ducks" gangs in San Francisco come from?

A. They were escaped convicts from Botany Bay, Australia.

◆

Q. What time was the Great Earthquake on April 18, 1906?

A. 5:16 A.M.

◆

Q. Who was pardoned in 1939 for his role in the Preparedness Day bombing?

A. Tom Mooney.

◆

Q. Where did General John Pershing's wife and three daughters die?

A. At the Presidio (in a 1915 fire).

◆

Q. What was the cost of building the Golden Gate Bridge?

A. $35,500,000.

◆

Q. Who was the first Mexican governor of California?

A. Luis Antonio Arguello.

◆

Q. Who founded the Ladies' Seamen's Friend Society?

A. Mrs. Rebecca H. Lambert.

Q. Who held the first Christian service in California in 1579?

A. Sir Francis Drake's chaplain.

———◆———

Q. What was the first capital of California following American occupation?

A. San Jose.

———◆———

Q. What was the first California legislature known as?

A. The "legislature of a thousand drinks."

———◆———

Q. Who is generally recognized as Stockton's founder?

A. Capt. Charles M. Webber.

———◆———

Q. Who was the last of the Pony Express riders?

A. William Campbell.

———◆———

Q. For whom was Fort Bragg named?

A. General Braxton Bragg.

———◆———

Q. What famous brothers once worked in the La Honda store?

A. Jim and Bob Younger.

Q. Who was the most famous and daring of the 1860s mail stage drivers?

A. "Cockeyed Charley" Parkhurst.

───◆───

Q. Who did "Cockeyed Charley" Parkhurst turn out to be?

A. A woman named Charlotte Parkhurst.

───◆───

Q. Who founded California's first sugar dynasty?

A. Claus Spreckels.

───◆───

Q. How many shots were fired in 1835 to overthrow Monterey?

A. One cannonball.

───◆───

Q. Who built the first Chatauqua in the West?

A. Methodist Episcopal Church members.

───◆───

Q. Who brought the Shaker sect to Klamath?

A. Jimmie Jacks, a local Indian.

───◆───

Q. What famed general was once stationed at Fort Humboldt?

A. Ulysses S. Grant.

Q. What bandit had a rock named for him?

A. Black Bart.

———◆———

Q. Into what two groups were Sausalito's early inhabitants divided?

A. "Wharf Rats" and "Hill Snobs."

———◆———

Q. During the Bear Flag Rebellion, how far did Alcade Juarez swim to escape capture?

A. Nine miles.

———◆———

Q. What Indian woman warned the town of Yreka of an impending attack?

A. Klamath Peggy.

———◆———

Q. Who cut off Joaquin Murrieta's head?

A. Bill Byrnes.

———◆———

Q. What founder of Chico ran for President of the U.S. on the Prohibition Party ticket?

A. Gen. John Bidwell.

———◆———

Q. Where were the Native Daughters of the Golden West organized in 1886?

A. Jackson.

Q. Who drew up the first code of miners' laws?

A. Col. J. D. Stevenson.

———◆———

Q. What events in Columbia described by Horace Greeley gave Wall Street its best-known terms?

A. The bull and bear fights.

———◆———

Q. What did the few survivors of the Donner party of the winter of 1846-47 eat to survive?

A. Their moccasins, boots, shoestrings, and each other.

———◆———

Q. When was the last run of the Pony Express?

A. November 1861.

———◆———

Q. What did the Golden Gate International Exposition commemorate?

A. The completion of the Golden Gate and San Francisco-Oakland Bay bridges.

———◆———

Q. Who was the first white child born in California?

A. Salvator Ignacio Linares.

———◆———

Q. When was the Presidio of San Francisco founded?

A. 1776.

Q. Who was the first American in California?

A. John Graham (he died the same day he arrived in Monterey).

———◆———

Q. When was the first Supreme Court of California formed?

A. 1840.

———◆———

Q. Who were the first Americans to be married in California?

A. Nancy Peterson and James Williams (from Missouri), 1846.

———◆———

Q. When did the ill-fated Donner party get halted by heavy snows?

A. October 31, 1846.

———◆———

Q. How many "Gold Rush" passengers did the first steamer *California* bring to San Francisco?

A. 365.

———◆———

Q. How much did postage on the Pony Express cost?

A. Five dollars a half-ounce.

———◆———

Q. What San Francisco mayor won a suit against *Look* magazine?

A. Joseph Alioto.

Q. Who led the 1836 revolution against Mexico to establish California's home rule?

A. Juan Bautista Alvarado.

◆

Q. Whose try for admission to the University of California, Davis, Medical School led to a Supreme Court decision on reverse discrimination?

A. Allen Paul Bakke.

◆

Q. What Georgia native became California's sixteenth governor?

A. Washington Bartlett.

◆

Q. Who was called the "conqueror of California"?

A. Robert Stockton.

◆

Q. Who brought camels to California?

A. Edward Fitzgerald Beale.

◆

Q. Who pardoned Warren Billings for his role in the San Francisco labor wars?

A. Governor Pat Brown.

◆

Q. How many city blocks of San Francisco were burned out after the Great Earthquake of 1906?

A. 497.

Q. What was the cost of building the California state capitol?

A. $2,600,000.

Q. What was the cost of restoring the state capitol?

A. $68,000,000.

Q. What does Prayerbook Cross in San Francisco commemorate?

A. The first English language worship service on the Pacific Coast.

Q. What woman member of the California Supreme Court once taught at Stanford Law School?

A. Rose Elizabeth Bird.

Q. Who was considered the greatest orator of all California governors?

A. Newton Booth.

Q. Who was called "Governor Moonbeam"?

A. Jerry Brown.

Q. What California senator's political career ended abruptly in a fatal duel?

A. David Colbreth Broderick.

Q. How did Governor Edmund Brown get his nickname "Pat"?

A. For his high school imitations of Patrick Henry.

Q. Who was called the "Blind Boss of San Francisco"?

A. Christopher Augustine Buckley.

Q. How many people first settled San Francisco?

A. 240.

Q. Who was convicted of the largest mass murder in California history?

A. Juan Corona.

Q. What event at the Marin County Courthouse caused Angela Davis to flee?

A. A shootout that left four people dead.

Q. What San Francisco mayor ended his political career as governor of Pennsylvania?

A. John White Geary.

Q. Known for his plaid tam-o-shanter, what California U.S. senator was once a leader of the Anti-Digit Dialing League?

A. Dr. S. I. Hayakawa.

Q. What member of the Red Family commune was drummed out for allegedly being a publicity-mongering political opportunist?

A. Tom Hayden.

Q. What preacher bought a former San Francisco synagogue for his People's Temple?

A. Jim Jones.

Q. What was the real name of El Dorado's Emperor Norton?

A. Joshua Abraham Norton.

Q. Where was the site of the 1846 Bear Flag Rebellion?

A. Sonoma.

Q. Who was attending Merrit Junior College in Oakland when he met Huey Newton and formed the Black Panther Party?

A. Bobby Seale.

Q. What San Francisco merchant now known by his first name sold the world's most popular pants?

A. Levi Strauss.

Q. What were the woodsmen who settled Scotia called?

A. "Blue Noses."

Q. Who built the railroad from San Francisco to Gilroy?

A. Henry Mayo Newhall.

———◆———

Q. How long did Milton Latham serve as California's sixth governor?

A. Five days (he then resigned to fill a Senate seat).

———◆———

Q. Who used the "junk-food" defense at his trial for the shooting of Harvey Milk and San Francisco Mayor George Moscone?

A. Dan White.

———◆———

Q. What bay area was discovered in 1775 by Spanish explorers and settled by Russians in 1809?

A. Bodega Bay.

———◆———

Q. Where is the Railway 1897 State Historical Park?

A. Jamestown.

———◆———

Q. Who was California's foremost crusader against "yellow slavery"?

A. Donaldina MacKenzie Cameron.

———◆———

Q. What town claims to have pioneered prohibition in California?

A. Lompoc.

ARTS & LITERATURE

C H A P T E R F O U R

Q. In what community did Bret Harte edit *Union* from 1858 to 1860?

A. Arcata.

———◆———

Q. The home/museum of painter Grace Carpenter Hudson is situated where?

A. Ukiah.

———◆———

Q. What was the first play to run in San Francisco's California Theater?

A. "Money."

———◆———

Q. Who immortalized Cannery Row?

A. John Steinbeck.

———◆———

Q. Pulitzer Prize-winning author William Saroyan was born and died in what California city?

A. Fresno.

Q. Who was the editor of the *Alta Californian?*

A. Bret Harte.

———◆———

Q. Where in California can one of the finest collections of Mono Indian basketwork and artifacts be viewed?

A. Sierra Mono Museum, North Fork.

———◆———

Q. Author Henry Miller made his home in what northern California area?

A. Big Sur.

———◆———

Q. Ansel Adams' home was in what California town?

A. Carmel.

———◆———

Q. What was the name of poet Robinson Jeffers' hand-built house?

A. TOR House.

———◆———

Q. Who was the first California sculptor to be recognized abroad?

A. Deaf artist Douglas Tilden.

———◆———

Q. What is the only museum in the United States devoted to the Victorian Period?

A. The American Victoriam Museum, Nevada City.

Q. What city has Jack London's log cabin and other water-front haunts of the author?

A. Oakland.

———————◆———————

Q. What was the Sacramento Valley's pioneer newspaper?

A. *Placer Times*.

———————◆———————

Q. What famous Oakland poet lived in the Park's "Abbey"?

A. Joaquin Miller.

———————◆———————

Q. Where in Petaluma is the world's only free-standing glass dome?

A. The Carnegie Library.

———————◆———————

Q. In what year did the University of California graduate its first class?

A. 1873.

———————◆———————

Q. John Steinbeck's birthplace is preserved in what California city?

A. Salinas.

———————◆———————

Q. Where can the world's finest examples of carousel art be seen?

A. The American Carousel Museum, Fisherman's Wharf.

Q. Where is Bret Harte's boyhood home?

A. Oakland.

———◆———

Q. Who was the famous "fighting editor" of the *Daily Evening Bulletin"?*

A. James King of William.

———◆———

Q. Where is Jack London's grave?

A. Glen Ellen.

———◆———

Q. Where is the only study center in North America devoted solely to Beethoven?

A. San Jose Center for Beethoven Studies.

———◆———

Q. What magazine was founded in 1878 by the Southern Pacific Country?

A. *Sunset.*

———◆———

Q. In what languages was the *Alta Californian* printed?

A. Half English, half Spanish.

———◆———

Q. What was the setting for Cyra McFadden's book, *The Serial?*

A. Mill Valley.

Q. What was the first California institution to offer classes in higher learning?

A. University of Santa Clara.

Q. Where is an exact replica of Michelangelo's "Pietà" on display?

A. Church of the Resurrection, Sunnyvale.

Q. What was the first newspaper in San Francisco to publish the news of President Abraham Lincoln's assassination?

A. *The Dramatic Chronicle*.

Q. What did Francisco Palou's *Historical Memories of New California* record?

A. The mission work of the Franciscans.

Q. What town inspired Mark Twain to write "The Celebrated Jumping Frog of Calaveras County"?

A. Angels Camp.

Q. Who was California's first printer?

A. Augustin V. Zamorano.

Q. Where is the residence of John Muir, famed author and conservationist?

A. Martinez.

Q. Where did Robert Louis Stevenson write *Vendetta of the West?*

A. The "French Hotel" in Monterey, now called the Stevenson House.

———◆———

Q. Where is the annual Renaissance Pleasure Faire held?

A. Novato.

———◆———

Q. What name did William Randolph Hearst give to his San Simeon estate?

A. La Cuesta Encantada ("The Enchanted Hill").

———◆———

Q. Where is the annual Fats Waller Memorial Jazz Festival held?

A. Watsonville.

———◆———

Q. What was California's first eight-page daily newspaper?

A. San Francisco *Daily Examiner*.

———◆———

Q. Who established the Institute for the Study of Nonviolence in Carmel?

A. Joan Baez.

———◆———

Q. What was the first newspaper in California?

A. *The Californian*, Monterey.

Q. What author ran unsuccessfully for governor of California in 1934?

A. Upton Sinclair.

———◆———

Q. Where was famed New England poet Robert Frost born?

A. San Francisco.

———◆———

Q. Where was the birthplace of Joan Didion?

A. Sacramento.

———◆———

Q. What is Pauline Kael's hometown?

A. Petaluma.

———◆———

Q. What is the California state song?

A. "I Love You, California."

———◆———

Q. Who called the Sacramento-San Joaquin Central Valley the "Long Valley"?

A. John Steinbeck.

———◆———

Q. Where was Irving Stone born?

A. San Francisco.

Q. Whose memorabilia does the Silverado Museum in St. Helena house?

A. Robert Louis Stevenson's.

Q. What did the *Sacramento Bee* oppose in 1857?

A. Land monopoly.

Q. What Mormon Pioneer published the *California Star* in 1847?

A. Samuel Brannan.

Q. What was the first daily paper in California?

A. The *Alta Californian*.

Q. What *San Francisco Post* editor advocated the single-tax system?

A. Henry George.

Q. Which book described Jack London's fight with alcohol?

A. *John Barleycorn*.

Q. What was the first California radio station to broadcast the human voice?

A. KQW.

Q. Who was San Francisco's first famous book critic?

A. Joseph Henry Jackson.

------◆------

Q. What was the first girls' college in California?

A. Young Ladies' Seminary.

------◆------

Q. What was the first name of the University of California?

A. Contra Costa Academy.

------◆------

Q. When was the first public high school opened?

A. 1856.

------◆------

Q. What book written by Sir Francis Drake's nephew told of his uncle's discovery of California?

A. *The World Encompassed*.

------◆------

Q. When was the first theatrical performance given in San Francisco?

A. 1849.

------◆------

Q. Who has been called the "True Father of California Literature"?

A. Francisco Palou.

Q. What type of printing press was the *Alta Californian* printed on?

A. Ramage.

◆

Q. Who was the first KQW radio "star"?

A. Al Pearce.

◆

Q. What literary magazine published the letters of "Shirley"?

A. *The Pioneer.*

◆

Q. What was the first book in English dealing exclusively with California?

A. *The History of Upper and Lower California.*

◆

Q. Who wrote *Two Years Before the Mast?*

A. Richard Henry Dana.

◆

Q. Who wrote under the pen names of John P. Squibob and John Phoenix?

A. George H. Derby.

◆

Q. What was the *Golden Era?*

A. A literary journal devoted to mining, news, commerce, arts, and literature.

Q. Who published the San Francisco *Daily Examiner?*

A. William Randolph Hearst.

———◆———

Q. What radio station first broadcast "One Man's Family"?

A. KFRC.

———◆———

Q. What famed editor of the San Francisco *Bulletin* was instrumental in exposing political scandals?

A. Fremont Older.

———◆———

Q. For what California newspaper was Samuel Clemens a reporter in the late 1850s?

A. San Francisco *Call.*

———◆———

Q. Who wrote *Innocents Abroad?*

A. Mark Twain.

———◆———

Q. Where was Bret Harte's last California editorship that established his fame?

A. *The Overland Monthly.*

———◆———

Q. Who wrote *Ramona?*

A. Helen Hunt Jackson.

Q. What noted California writer disappeared in Mexico just prior to World War I?

A. Ambrose Bierce.

◆

Q. How old was Lotta Crabtree when she began her acting career?

A. Nine years.

◆

Q. What California poet was known for his "Purple Cow"?

A. Gelett Burgess.

◆

Q. Where did Robert Louis Stevenson and Mrs. Osbourne marry?

A. San Francisco.

◆

Q. What British journalist failed in his attempt to find a publisher for his works in San Francisco?

A. Rudyard Kipling.

◆

Q. Who first published verses by Bret Harte?

A. The *Golden Era*.

◆

Q. What was the first Chinese newspaper in California?

A. Gold Hills *News*.

Q. "The Man with the Hoe" made what poet famous?

A. Edwin Markham.

Q. Who founded the literary colony at Carmel?

A. George Sterling.

Q. Who wrote *McTeague* and *The Octopus?*

A. Frank Norris.

Q. Who wrote *Ruggles of Red Gap?*

A. Harry Leon Wilson.

Q. What San Francisco "oyster pirate" and longshoreman became the most spectacular literary figure of his time?

A. Jack London.

Q. What was the first black newspaper in California?

A. *The California Eagle.*

Q. What California author wrote the letters of "Shirley" that were published in *The Pioneer?*

A. Mrs. Laura A. K. Clapp.

Q. What famed journalist of the muckraking era was born in Sacramento?

A. Lincoln Steffens.

———————◆———————

Q. Where did Gertrude Stein live during her early childhood?

A. The San Francisco Bay area.

———————◆———————

Q. Where did the Bohemian Club put on its plays?

A. In a redwood grove near Monte Rio.

———————◆———————

Q. *Land of the Rain* was the first novel of what woman member of the northern California literati?

A. Mary Hunter Austin.

———————◆———————

Q. What did Robinson Jeffers erect in Carmel?

A. A stone tower.

———————◆———————

Q. Where were the "convict-writers" imprisoned?

A. San Quentin.

———————◆———————

Q. Who was the first artist to popularize the distinctiveness of the California landscape?

A. William Smith Jewett.

Q. What artist designed the bear on the California State Flag?

A. Charles C. Nahl.

———◆———

Q. What did the Tivoli Opera House begin as?

A. A public beer garden.

———◆———

Q. When was the first symphony concert performed in San Francisco?

A. 1865.

———◆———

Q. How many people did San Francisco's Grand Opera House seat?

A. Over 3,000.

———◆———

Q. Whose "Symphony in D Minor" won the 1932 Pulitzer Prize?

A. Ernst Bacon.

———◆———

Q. Where is the home of the Defense Language Institute?

A. The Presidio, Monterey.

———◆———

Q. Where did Ernest Bloch write the symphonic suite "America"?

A. Marin County.

Q. What San Francisco club founded in 1872 was composed of painters, artists, and writers?

A. The Bohemian Club.

———◆———

Q. What author of *Progress and Poverty* was called the "Prophet of San Francisco"?

A. Henry George.

———◆———

Q. What was the first building erected in California for theatrical performances?

A. The Eagle Theater, Sacramento.

———◆———

Q. Where did Lotta Crabtree make her first dramatic appearance?

A. Petaluma.

———◆———

Q. Where did Rube Goldberg attend college?

A. University of California.

———◆———

Q. What artist sketched day and night to chronicle the 1906 San Francisco earthquake and fire on the 12x30-foot "The Fire"?

A. Charles Dorman Robinson.

———◆———

Q. Who designed the California state capitol?

A. F. M. Butler.

Q. What famous dancer was well known in San Francisco?

A. Isadora Duncan.

———◆———

Q. What was the setting of the *Maltese Falcon?*

A. San Francisco.

———◆———

Q. Who had a theater built by the public to keep him from ending his career?

A. Edwin Booth.

———◆———

Q. What handicap did sculptor Douglas Tilden overcome?

A. He was a deaf-mute.

———◆———

Q. What did Lotta Crabtree give to the city of San Francisco in 1875?

A. Lotta's Fountain (for public use).

———◆———

Q. What was the *Order of E Clampus Vitas?*

A. The gold miners' burlesque fraternity.

———◆———

Q. Why was James King of William so named?

A. To distinguish himself from other James Kings.

Q. Who wrote "The Old Oaken Bucket"?

A. Samuel Woodworth.

———◆———

Q. Where was the center for the Ancient and Mystical order of the Rosy Cross?

A. Rosicrucian Park and Headquarters in San Jose.

———◆———

Q. Where is the home of the College of the Pacific?

A. Stockton.

———◆———

Q. Where was the first open-air community theater?

A. Forest Theater in Carmel.

———◆———

Q. What were the two-week summer encampments of the Bohemian Club called?

A. High Jinks.

———◆———

Q. How many words did Jack London try to write each day?

A. 1,000.

———◆———

Q. Who was the "Holy Man of Santa Clara"?

A. Fray Maguin de Catala.

Q. Where did Joaquin Miller write his first poem?

A. Deadwood.

———◆———

Q. Who memorialized Fiddletown in his writings?

A. Bret Harte.

———◆———

Q. Where did Leland Stanford earn his money to endow the university that bears his name?

A. As one of the "Big Four" of the Central Pacific Railroad.

———◆———

Q. Where in San Andreas is the place that also claims to have inspired Mark Twain's "Jumping Frog" story?

A. The barroom of the Metropolitan Hotel.

———◆———

Q. What town, then known as Cherokee Flat, was the setting of Bret Harte's "To the Pliscene Skull"?

A. Altaville.

———◆———

Q. Who was California's first poet laureate?

A. Ina Coolbrith.

———◆———

Q. In what year did the San Francisco Ballet first produce a full-length *Swan Lake?*

A. 1940.

Q. Who has been called the dean of American nature photographers?

A. Ansel Adams.

---◆---

Q. Who founded the humor magazine for the University of California at Berkeley campus?

A. Earle C. Anthony.

---◆---

Q. Who was California's first "liberated" woman author?

A. Gertrude Atherton.

---◆---

Q. Who published a 39-volume history of the Pacific Slope?

A. Hubert Howe Bancroft.

---◆---

Q. Who called San Francisco a "moral penal colony"?

A. Ambrose Bierce.

---◆---

Q. Who gave the Greek theater to the University of California at Berkeley?

A. William Randolph Hearst.

---◆---

Q. Where is the Bade Institute of Biblical Archaeology?

A. Pacific School of Religion, Berkeley.

Q. Where did Robert Louis Stevenson honeymoon?

A. Mount St. Helena.

◆

Q. When did construction begin on the Hearst Mansion at San Simeon?

A. 1919.

◆

Q. What city inspired John Steinbeck's *Sweet Thursday?*

A. Monterey.

◆

Q. What famed journalist's father once owned the governor's mansion?

A. Lincoln Steffens.

◆

Q. Where is the "Hat in Three Stages of Landing" sculpture by Claes Oldenburg?

A. Salinas.

◆

Q. Where is the annual Cabrillo Music Festival held?

A. Aptos.

◆

Q. Where is the Snoopy Gallery?

A. Santa Rosa.

Q. Where is the annual Ox Roast and Art Show held?

A. Sonoma.

———◆———

Q. Who has been called the "J. D. Salinger of the Hippie Generation"?

A. Richard Brautigan.

———◆———

Q. What well-known author was a major contributor to the *Alta Californian?*

A. Mark Twain.

———◆———

Q. Where was Ursula Le Guin born?

A. Berkeley.

———◆———

Q. What sculptor was called San Francisco's cultural mascot for nearly 50 years?

A. Benny Bufano.

———◆———

Q. What San Franciscan coined the term *beatnik?*

A. Herb Caen.

———◆———

Q. Who constructed the "Running Fence"?

A. Christo.

Q. Who wrote *Soul on Ice* and *Soul on Fire?*

A. Eldridge Cleaver.

———◆———

Q. Who financed, among others, the Ben Franklin fountain in San Francisco?

A. Henry Daniel Cogswell.

———◆———

Q. Who was the first public librarian in Oakland?

A. Ina Coolbrith.

———◆———

Q. What musician pioneered the use of tone clusters and "elastic form"?

A. Henry Dixon Cowell.

———◆———

Q. What future Pulitzer Prize-winner edited *Aperitif* magazine from 1933 to 1936?

A. Stanton Delaplane.

———◆———

Q. What writer did Joan Didion marry?

A. John Gregory Dunne.

———◆———

Q. What artist did Dorothea Lange wed?

A. Maynard Dixon.

Q. How old was Isadora Duncan when she left San Francisco?

A. 17 years.

———◆———

Q. What was the first exclusively paperback bookstore in the United States?

A. City Lights Bookstore, San Francisco.

———◆———

Q. What poet was one of the organizers of the first "Be-In" in Golden Gate Park in 1959?

A. Allen Ginsberg.

———◆———

Q. What Elinor Glyn novel was the *Peyton Place* of 1907?

A. *Three Weeks*.

———◆———

Q. Who built Fillmore West?

A. Bill Graham.

———◆———

Q. Who wrote *The True Believer* in 1951?

A. Eric Hoffer.

———◆———

Q. What chronicler of the "beat" generation once worked as a Southern Pacific brakeman in San Francisco?

A. Jack Kerouac.

Q. Who was the *San Francisco Examiner*'s answer to Nellie Bly?

A. Annie Laurie.

Q. What was the last major project of Frank Lloyd Wright?

A. The Marin County Civic Center.

Q. Who designed Wyntoon, Phoebe Hearst's northern California castle?

A. Bernard Ralph Maybeck.

Q. The Supreme Court ruled that what Big Sur resident's books could be published?

A. Henry Miller.

Q. Whose 1977 memoir of life in the radical underground was titled *A Fine Old Conflict?*

A. Jessica Mitford.

Q. What University of California at Berkeley graduate became the first licensed woman architect in California?

A. Julia Morgan.

Q. Who earned his Ph.D. from University of California, Santa Cruz, with the thesis, *The FBI War against the Black Panthers?*

A. Huey Newton.

Q. What San Francisco-born heiress' first novel was *Mother*?

A. Kathleen Thompson Norris (1911).

———◆———

Q. What book established Anita Loos as the "Colette of American Sexual Comedy"?

A. *Gentlemen Prefer Blondes*.

———◆———

Q. What San Francisco building was designed by George Herbert Wyman, a novice with no training in design or construction?

A. The Bradbury Building.

———◆———

Q. The dome of what California courthouse has a statue of Minerva, the Roman goddess of wisdom?

A. Merced.

———◆———

Q. Where was painter and writer Martha Joanne Alf born on August 13, 1930?

A. Berkeley.

———◆———

Q. Santa Clara-born sculptor David M. Bottini is best known for his work in what two media?

A. Steel and bronze.

———◆———

Q. What Oakland-born curator served as director of the Haggin Museum in Stockton from 1971 to 1986?

A. Keith Elkins Dennison.

SPORTS & LEISURE

CHAPTER FIVE

Q. The Giants moved to San Francisco in what year?

A. 1958.

———◆———

Q. Where do the Golden State Warriors play their home games?

A. Oakland Coliseum Arena.

———◆———

Q. The Oakland Raiders won their first Super Bowl against what team?

A. Minnesota Vikings (Super Bowl XI, 32-14).

———◆———

Q. What California town took its name from a card game?

A. Mugginsville (from the game of Muggins).

———◆———

Q. Quarterback John Brodie played for what Northern California college, 1954-56?

A. Stanford.

Q. Northstar at Tahoe is the site of what unique February competiton?

A. Firefighters' Winter Games.

———◆———

Q. Northern California native Lefty Gomez spent his entire major league career with what baseball club?

A. New York Yankees.

———◆———

Q. In what year did the San Francisco 49ers win their first Super Bowl?

A. 1982.

———◆———

Q. To what sole purpose was Box Canyon Dam and Lake created?

A. Recreation.

———◆———

Q. Where may one enjoy DJ's Snowmobile Adventures?

A. Mammoth Lakes.

———◆———

Q. What town is known as the "Bicycle Capital of the World" because it has more than 40,000 bicycles for its 40,000-plus citizens?

A. Davis.

———◆———

Q. What is called the "most spectacular walk in the world"?

A. The Promenade, 3½ miles of San Francisco's northern shoreline.

Q. What San Francisco 49er set a single-game Super Bowl record for most points by scoring three touchdowns?

A. Roger Craig (Super Bowl XIX).

———◆———

Q. Stanford University's William McColl played for what professional football team, 1952-59?

A. Chicago Bears.

———◆———

Q. Legendary Giant Willie Mays was known by what nickname?

A. The "Say Hey" Kid.

———◆———

Q. What northern California town has an annual Cornish Christmas Festival?

A. Grass Valley.

———◆———

Q. What northern Californian built the race track that became Santa Anita?

A. Lucky Baldwin.

———◆———

Q. What baseball team was called the Wobblies?

A. Folsom Prison.

———◆———

Q. What four-mile-long scenic railway is situated near Yosemite National Park?

A. Yosemite Mountain Sugar Pine Railroad.

Q. In what year did Stanford first play in the Rose Bowl?

A. 1902 (the first year the game was held).

———◆———

Q. What San Francisco-born 1st baseman won his eleventh straight National League Golden Glove award in 1988?

A. Keith Hernandez.

———◆———

Q. Where is the California Cup Regatta held?

A. Modesto.

———◆———

Q. In 1970 what Giants batter set a National League record for most strike-outs in a single season?

A. Bobby Bonds (189).

———◆———

Q. What Sunnyvale native became the 1986 National and World Figure Skating Champion?

A. Brian Boitano.

———◆———

Q. Where are the World Wrist-Wrestling Championships held each year?

A. Petaluma.

———◆———

Q. In 1954 UCLA running back Paul Cameron played for what NFL team?

A. Pittsburgh Steelers.

Q. During what celebration at Sebastopol is the 10-K Apple Juice Run held?

A. The Apple Blossom Festival.

------◆------

Q. Where is the Tehoma County Fair held?

A. Red Bluff.

------◆------

Q. What two Stanford coaches have been named Coach of the Year by the American Football Coaches Association?

A. Clark Shaughnessy (1940) and Chuck Taylor (1951).

------◆------

Q. What Oakland native was elected to the Baseball Hall of Fame in 1980?

A. Ernie Lombardi.

------◆------

Q. Northern California-born Tom Seaver made his major league debut with what baseball club?

A. New York Mets (1967).

------◆------

Q. Where is the annual International Airshow held?

A. Salinas.

------◆------

Q. What is the length of the Big Sur International Marathon?

A. 26 miles (Big Sur to Carmel).

Q. What exciting, reptilian racing event is held at Doyle?

A. Doyle Days World Champion Lizard Races.

———————✦———————

Q. How many NCAA basketball championships has the University of San Francisco won?

A. Two.

———————✦———————

Q. Where are the Inglenook Vineyards?

A. Rutherford.

———————✦———————

Q. What unique celebration is held in April at Fort Humbolt State Historic Park?

A. Steam Donkey Days Festival.

———————✦———————

Q. Where do the San Francisco Giants play their home games?

A. Candlestick Park.

———————✦———————

Q. What major theme park is in Santa Clara?

A. Great America.

———————✦———————

Q. What California community bills itself as having "The Best in the West Rodeo"?

A. Oakdale.

Q. Petaluma is known for what spring celebration?

A. Butter and Eggs Day Parade.

Q. What Stanford basketball coach led his 1942 team to an NCAA championship?

A. Everett Dean (coached 1939-51).

Q. What coastal community hosts the Scottish Highland Games?

A. Monterey.

Q. In what bowl game did Stanford defeat Georgia, 25-22, on December 31, 1978?

A. Bluebonnet.

Q. Where is California's only seashore amusement park?

A. Santa Cruz's Beach Boardwalk.

Q. Redding-born center Melvin Hein played for what NFL team, 1931-45?

A. New York Giants.

Q. Albany is the location of what thoroughbred race track?

A. Golden Gate Fields.

Q. Where is the annual Avenue of the Giants Marathon held?

A. Garberville.

———◆———

Q. What are the colors of the Golden State Warriors?

A. Gold and Blue.

———◆———

Q. What baseball Hall of Fame legend died in Santa Cruz on December 18, 1974?

A. Harry Hooper.

———◆———

Q. Fort Funston on the Pacific Ocean side of San Francisco is an excellent spot for what aerial sport?

A. Hang-gliding.

———◆———

Q. What civic organization sponsors California's only "damboree"?

A. Shasta Dam Area Chamber of Commerce.

———◆———

Q. Where is the West's busiest race track?

A. Bay Meadows, San Mateo.

———◆———

Q. The Matsen Ramsey Stockhorse Jubilee is hosted by what California community?

A. Alturas.

Q. The Lambtown USA Festival is celebrated in what California community?

A. Sacramento.

Q. The World Championship Cribbage Tournament is held in what northern California town?

A. Quincy.

Q. In 1961 what baseball team set a record for most runs in the ninth inning of a game?

A. Giants (12).

Q. What San Francisco-born athlete played for California in the 1949 Rose Bowl and for the New York Yankees in a World Series?

A. Jackie Jensen.

Q. Where is the world's only man-made floating tropical island?

A. Forbes Island, Sausalito.

Q. Six-foot, ten-inch Clyde Lee wore what number when he played for the Golden State Warriors?

A. 43.

Q. Where was the site of the 1960 Winter Olympics?

A. Squaw Valley.

Q. What track and field competition is held in Modesto each May?

A. S & W Invitational Track Meet.

◆

Q. Where is the home of "Jelly Belly" jelly beans?

A. Herman Goelitz Candy Company, Fairfield.

◆

Q. What museum maintains a collection of horse snow-shoes?

A. Sierra Museum, Downieville.

◆

Q. In 1969 what Giants batter received the most intentional walks in a single season?

A. Willie McCovey.

◆

Q. San Francisco hosts what footrace known to be the world's largest?

A. Bay-to-Bay Breakers.

◆

Q. Fort Bragg is the site of what sanctioned cooking contest?

A. Mendocino Territory Whistle Punk Chili Cook-Off.

◆

Q. What Sacramento-born shortstop set fielding records in 1971 with the Philadelphia Phillies?

A. Larry Bowa.

Q. What former College of the Pacific quarterback led the AFL in passing efficiency in his rookie year?

A. Tom Flores.

◆

Q. Where is the Trail of Tall Tales featuring chainsaw-carved redwood sculptures?

A. Trees of Mystery Park, Klamath.

◆

Q. What Fresno-born Oakland Raider had a string of 25 straight games in which he threw touchdown passes?

A. Daryle Lamonica (1969-70).

◆

Q. In what year was O.J. Simpson traded to the San Francisco 49ers?

A. 1978.

◆

Q. Where is the Allen Knight Maritime Museum?

A. Monterey.

◆

Q. What Rodeo-born pitcher won the most World Series games without a defeat?

A. Lefty Gomez (6).

◆

Q. Where is the annual Grape Festival and National Wine Show held?

A. Lodi.

Q. In 1948 what California native set an American League record for most putouts by an outfielder?

A. Dominic DiMaggio (503).

———◆———

Q. Where is the site of the High Sierra Regatta?

A. Huntington Lake.

———◆———

Q. Native American dance competition is featured at what Susanville celebration?

A. Lassen County Pow Wow.

———◆———

Q. Hank Ketcham helped create what Monterey Park?

A. Dennis the Menace Playground.

———◆———

Q. What participant in the famous "Black Sox" scandal died in Calistoga, December 13, 1970?

A. Charles ("Chick") Gandil.

———◆———

Q. What community is the site of the Midsummer Scandinavian Festival and Barbecue?

A. Ferndale.

———◆———

Q. What award goes to the winner of the annual Stanford/California football game?

A. The Axe.

Q. What Stanford athlete was the only freshman named to the All PAC-10 first team in the 1985-86 basketball season?

A. Todd Lichti.

◆

Q. Bill Russell led the University of San Francisco Dons to what basketball record during the 1954-55 and 1955-56 seasons?

A. 57-1.

◆

Q. Where can the original "Golden Spike" that completed the first U.S. transcontinental railroad be seen?

A. Leland Stanford, Jr., Museum, Palo Alto.

◆

Q. How long were Martinez-born Joe DiMaggio and actress Marilyn Monroe married?

A. Nine months.

◆

Q. What Japanese celebration is held in Fresno each July?

A. Obon-Odori Festival.

◆

Q. What has been called the "biggest little county fair in the Sacramento Valley"?

A. Glen County Fair.

◆

Q. What was the nickname of former Giants 1st baseman Willie McCovey?

A. "Stretch."

Q. The Golden Bears of the University of California, Berkeley, play their home basketball games on what court?

A. Harmon Arena.

———◆———

Q. What served as the home field for the San Francisco 49ers prior to their move to Candlestick Park?

A. Kezar Stadium.

———◆———

Q. A challenging 10-K course and a 1.8-mile course both are part of what annual Heraldsburg racing event?

A. Fitch Mountain Footrace.

———◆———

Q. Northern California native Frank Chance was considered one of baseball's greatest at what position?

A. First base.

———◆———

Q. Where is the National Coyote Howling Contest held?

A. Coulterville.

———◆———

Q. What San Lorenzo High School graduate played tackle for the Miami Dolphins, 1968-73?

A. Manuel Fernandez.

———◆———

Q. Where is the Parade of Champions held?

A. Santa Clara.

Q. Where is the Festival of Saws held?

A. Santa Cruz.

———◆———

Q. Where is the home of the Sacramento Kings?

A. Arco Arena.

———◆———

Q. What Red Bluff event features boat races in excess of 200 m.p.h.?

A. Memorial Day Boat Drags.

———◆———

Q. What Merced-born major leaguer had a 1.27 ERA with the Los Angeles Dodgers in 1972?

A. Jim Brewer.

———◆———

Q. What San Francisco-born football player was the Philadelphia Eagles all-time scorer at his retirement in 1970?

A. Sam Baker.

———◆———

Q. What is the average temperature during a night game at Candlestick Park?

A. 53 degrees.

———◆———

Q. Coalinga is the site of what unusual races and celebration?

A. Horned Toad Derby.

Q. Where can the Union Pacific *Centennial,* billed as the world's largest diesel locomotive, be seen?

A. Portola Railroad Museum.

———◆———

Q. Where is the Alameda County Fair held?

A. Pleasanton.

———◆———

Q. Where are the West Coast's largest competition crab races held?

A. Crescent City.

———◆———

Q. World-class athletes compete each May in what San Jose track and field meet?

A. Bruce Jenner Classic.

———◆———

Q. What museum has over 140 vintage autos, including every Ford model from 1903 through 1952?

A. Towe Ford Museum, Sacramento.

———◆———

Q. In 1970 what Niles native tied the record for most consecutive errorless games in the major leagues?

A. Bud Harrelson (54).

———◆———

Q. Taylorsville is the home of what rodeo?

A. Silver Buckle Rodeo.

Q. Where is the mammoth California Rodeo held each year?

A. Salinas.

———◆———

Q. In how many World Series did Frank Crosetti participate as a player and a manager?

A. 23 (8 as a player, 15 as a manager).

———◆———

Q. What Stanford Cardinal became the school's first Heisman Trophy winner?

A. Jim Plunkett (1970).

———◆———

Q. The finest calamari is served at what Monterey celebration?

A. Monterey Squid Festival.

———◆———

Q. What organization sponsors the Valentine's Week Cross-Country Ski Race at Alturas?

A. Warner Mountain Sports Association.

———◆———

Q. Built in 1924, what Santa Cruz Beach Boardwalk ride still thrills its riders?

A. The Giant Dipper roller coaster.

———◆———

Q. What Oakland native was the first black quarterback to play regularly in the NFL?

A. Marlin Briscoe.

Q. What celebration is called the "only water festival of its kind west of the Mississippi"?

A. Sacramento Water Festival.

———◆———

Q. What California town is famous for its balloon rides over the Napa Valley?

A. Yountville.

———◆———

Q. What Santa Cruz competition attracts top surfers from California and Hawaii?

A. The Annual Longboard Club Invitational.

———◆———

Q. Nelson Briles was born in what northern California community?

A. Dorris.

———◆———

Q. Where is the Taylor California Cellars 10-K Run held each March?

A. Gonzales.

———◆———

Q. What sports figure was news director of the University of San Francisco, 1952-55?

A. Pete Rozelle.

———◆———

Q. Where is the annual Fireman's Muster held?

A. Sonora.

Q. What team is the only Super Bowl Champion to have had a losing record the previous season?

A. The San Francisco 49ers.

———◆———

Q. Where is the Western America Skisport Museum?

A. Soda Springs.

———◆———

Q. What northern California event features a one-of-a-kind race with people-powered contraptions?

A. The Great Arcata to Ferndale Cross-Country Kinetic Sculpture Race.

———◆———

Q. San Francisco 49er quarterback Joe Montana's salary reportedly exceeded what figure by 1989?

A. $1.1 million.

———◆———

Q. What tale-telling event is held at Mariposa?

A. Gold Country Yarns.

———◆———

Q. Where is the San Joaquin County Fair held each September?

A. Stockton.

———◆———

Q. At the Susanville Open Golf Tournament, a hole-in-one wins what prize?

A. A car.

Q. Who was the youngest baseball player ever to win the Major League Most Valuable Player award?

A. Vida Blue (age 22).

———◆———

Q. Where is the California State Fair held each year?

A. Sacramento.

———◆———

Q. How many Major League batting titles were won by northern Californian Harry Heilmann?

A. Four (1921, 1923, 1925, and 1927).

———◆———

Q. Where is the California Balloon Festival held?

A. Madera.

———◆———

Q. What community is host to the California State Old-Time Fiddlers' Northern Regional Championship?

A. Oroville.

———◆———

Q. What 1936 Santa Clara quarterback led his team to a 21-14 Sugar Bowl victory over LSU?

A. Nello ("Flash") Falaschi.

———◆———

Q. Of what material were the poker chips used by the Bonanza Kings made?

A. Solid ivory.

Q. What famed "gentleman" boxer trained in San Rafael?

A. James J. Corbett.

———◆———

Q. What was the first commercial racing track in California?

A. Tanforan Race Track.

———◆———

Q. Major leaguer Buck Buckner was born in what northern California city?

A. Vallejo.

———◆———

Q. On what body of water is the site of the Great Stern-wheeler race held?

A. Lake Tahoe.

———◆———

Q. Where was the first California ski club organized in 1913?

A. Truckee.

———◆———

Q. Who was Stanford's top rebounder during the 1987-88 basketball season?

A. Howard Wright.

———◆———

Q. The Santa Clara Raiders Unlimited sponsor what 10-mile cross-country motorcycle racing event near Hollister?

A. The Hare Scrambles.

Q. What Oakland hurler was Most Valuable Player of the earthquake-delayed 1989 World Series?

A. Dave Stewart.

Q. What San Francisco 49er set a Super Bowl record with 215 receiving yards and 11 receptions?

A. Jerry Rice (Super Bowl XXIII).

Q. Northern California native Ewell Blackwell was given what nickname due to his pitching style?

A. "Whip."

Q. Pony Express Days are celebrated in what northern California community?

A. McKinleyville.

Q. In what California town are sled dog races held each year?

A. Truckee.

Q. What St. Mary's College football player served as head coach at Annapolis, 1950-58?

A. Eddie Erdelatz.

Q. What Fresno-born pitcher had his best year in 1947 with a 22-8 record?

A. Ewell Blackwell.

Q. What celebration and spaghetti feed is held at Sutter Creek?

A. Italian Picnic and Parade.

Q. Where is the annual Whaleboat Regatta held?

A. Vallejo.

Q. What San Francisco-born major leaguer became the first player to become the commissioner of the American League?

A. Joe Cronin.

Q. Where was famed tennis player Don Budge born?

A. Oakland.

Q. Who became the 29th head football coach of Stanford University in 1989?

A. Denny Green.

Q. What Indian festival at Janesville celebrates the survival of winter?

A. Annual Bear Dance.

Q. What millionaire who retired to Pebble Beach began a second career as the sports wizard of northern California?

A. Jack Kent Cooke.

Q. What San Francisco-born 1st baseman led the National League in home runs with 34 and in RBIs with 120 in 1941?

A. Dolph Camilli.

---◆---

Q. Where was the James Corbett-Joe Choynski fight held?

A. South Hampton Bay.

---◆---

Q. Francesco Stefano Pizzola was the original name of what San Francisco-born outfielder?

A. Frank Stephan ("Ping") Bodie.

---◆---

Q. Where is Undersea World?

A. Crescent City.

---◆---

Q. Featuring 280 kilometers of groomed cross-country trails, what is North America's largest ski resort?

A. Royal Gorge Cross-Country Ski Resort.

---◆---

Q. What Davis native had the smallest feet in the major league at the time of his 1931-45 career?

A. Myreil Hoag (size 4 right, size 4½ left).

---◆---

Q. Where is the Plane of Fame Air Museum?

A. Chino.

Q. The annual Highway 50 Wagon Train re-creation of the original Sierra crossing by pioneers on the Emigrant Trail runs between what two points?

A. Nevada and Placerville.

———◆———

Q. Joe DiMaggio started his professional career in the Pacific Coast League with what team?

A. San Francisco Seals.

———◆———

Q. What town celebrates Weihnachtsmarkt, the feast day of St. Nicholas?

A. Carmel.

———◆———

Q. What fair is Roseville home to?

A. Placer County Fair.

———◆———

Q. What famous hot springs resort founded in 1859 is operating today?

A. Calistoga.

———◆———

Q. What Mill Valley event is the second oldest cross-country race in America?

A. Dipsea Race.

———◆———

Q. What is the site of the World's Largest Salmon Barbecue?

A. Fort Bragg.

Q. Baseball great Harry Hooper was Postmaster of what northern California community for 25 years?

A. Capitola.

Q. Who caught Joe Montana's winning touchdown with 34 seconds remaining in Super Bowl XXIII?

A. John Taylor.

Q. The oldest continuous rodeo in California is held annually in what town?

A. Willits.

Q. What Berkeley-born tennis queen won eight Wimbledon singles titles?

A. Helen Wills Moody Roark.

Q. Sacramento-born Stan Hack played in the major leagues for 16 years, including four World Series, for what club?

A. Chicago Cubs.

Q. What 2,000-acre ski facility is situated 12 miles west of South Lake Tahoe?

A. Sierra Ski Ranch.

Q. Where is the Amador County Museum?

A. Jackson.

Q. Berkeley native Billy Martin played for eleven years in the major leagues with what clubs?

A. New York Yankees, Kansas City As, Detroit Tigers, Cleveland Indians, Cincinnati Reds, Milwaukee Braves, and Minnesota Twins.

Q. What Fresno-born baseball Hall of Fame great was known as "Peerless Leader"?

A. Frank Chance.

Q. Where is the Billy Jones Wildcat Railroad?

A. Los Gatos.

Q. What three Stanford players have rushed for over 1,000 yards in one season?

A. Darrin Nelson, Brad Muster, and Jon Volpe.

Q. Where is the Oakwood Lake Water Theme Park?

A. Manteca.

Q. Where is the home of the San Francisco Yacht Club?

A. Belvedere.

Q. Martinez native Joe DiMaggio was known by what nickname?

A. "Yankee Clipper."

Q. When is the Gold Country Fair held in Auburn?

A. September.

———◆———

Q. Pro soccer's Danny Payne and Dave Morrison received their starts in what city?

A. Livermore.

———◆———

Q. What community starts its Western Stampede by driving cattle through its streets?

A. Chowchilla.

———◆———

Q. San Jose native Bob Meusel played for what clubs during his major league career?

A. New York Yankees and Cincinnati Reds.

———◆———

Q. Where can visitors see chocker setting, double hand bucking, and log birling?

A. The North Fork Loggers Jamboree.

———◆———

Q. On August 4, 1985, what Fresno native became the seventeenth pitcher in major league history to win 300 games?

A. Tom Seaver.

———◆———

Q. The Hangtown Pro Rodeo is held in what Gold Country community?

A. Placerville.

Q. What is The Barnyard in Carmel?

A. A recreational shopping area.

———◆———

Q. What city holds an annual Artichoke Festival?

A. Castroville.

———◆———

Q. In 1985 Keith Hernandez set a major league record with how many game-winning RBIs?

A. 24.

———◆———

Q. The Kansas City Athletics moved to Oakland in what year?

A. 1968.

———◆———

Q. San Jose-born quarterback Bob Berry played for what professional football teams?

A. Minnesota Vikings (1965-67, 68) and Atlanta Falcons (1968-72).

———◆———

Q. Where is the Contra Costa County Fair held?

A. Antioch.

———◆———

Q. What California golf tournament was previously known as "The Crosby?"

A. AT&T Pebble Beach National Pro-Am Tournament.

Q. What San Francisco native New York Yankee hit two grand slams and drove in eleven runs in a 1936 game?

A. Tony Lazzeri.

——————◆——————

Q. Where can the 5,000-light chain, "Necklace of Lights," be seen?

A. Surrounding Lake Merritt in Oakland.

——————◆——————

Q. Where is the Orchard Waterslide?

A. Modesto.

——————◆——————

Q. Oakland native Ernie Lombardi played what position in the major leagues?

A. Catcher.

——————◆——————

Q. When was the "Human Wave" first seen in a stadium?

A. October 15, 1981 (seventh game of the playoffs between the A's and the Yankees).

——————◆——————

Q. What resort was noted for its "champagne baths"?

A. Vichy Springs Resort.

——————◆——————

Q. Los Gatos native Harold Chase was known in the major leagues by what nickname?

A. Prince Hal.

SCIENCE & NATURE

C H A P T E R   S I X

Q. What California cavern is known for the sounds that emanate from its entrance?

A. Moaning Cavern, Vallecito.

———◆———

Q. Mount Shasta, an inactive volcano, is considered by some to be what lost continent?

A. Mu, the Pacific's Atlantis.

———◆———

Q. The Lava Bed National Monument near Tule Lake consists of how many lava caves, lava tubes, and ice caves?

A. Over 300.

———◆———

Q. Where is the Upside-Down Tree?

A. Trees of Mystery, Klamath.

———◆———

Q. How long is the Golden Gate Bridge?

A. 4,200 feet.

Q. What is the oldest living laurel tree in California?

A. The Jepson Laurel at the north end of Crystal Springs Lake (at least 580 years old).

———◆———

Q. How tall is Coit Tower in San Francisco?

A. 210 feet.

———◆———

Q. Which park has the largest remaining stand of virgin redwood in the world?

A. Humboldt Redwoods State Park.

———◆———

Q. Who was the "plant wizard"?

A. Luther Burbank.

———◆———

Q. What is the California state animal?

A. California grizzly bear (now extinct).

———◆———

Q. What California community is called the "Bartlett Pear Capital"?

A. Kelseyville.

———◆———

Q. Freak dwarfed pines and cypress trees grow where?

A. Pygmy Forest, Eureka.

Q. In what year was San Francisco's Great Earthquake and Fire?

A. 1906.

◆

Q. What California town is built entirely of redwood lumber?

A. Scotia.

◆

Q. Where is the world's tallest tree situated?

A. Tall Trees Grove, Redwood National Park (367.8 feet).

◆

Q. California gray whales migrate during which months?

A. December through April.

◆

Q. What two-mile-long linear accelerator generates the highest energy electron beams in the world?

A. The Stanford Linear Accelerator Center in Menlo Park.

◆

Q. What is the nation's largest urban wildlife refuge?

A. San Francisco Bay National Wildlife Refuge (20,000 acres).

◆

Q. The General Grant, the "Nation's Christmas Tree," is in what California park?

A. King's Canyon National Park.

Q. Where can rare Japanese koi fish be seen?

A. Japanese Friendship Garden in San Jose.

———◆———

Q. Of what is the James Johnston House in Half Moon Bay constructed?

A. Mortise and tenon fastened together with wooden pegs.

———◆———

Q. A large grove of giant redwoods is named for which U.S. President?

A. William McKinley.

———◆———

Q. Daffodil Hill in Amador County has how many flowers?

A. More than 300,000.

———◆———

Q. What was the "world's first glass curtain-walled structure"?

A. Hallidie Building, San Francisco.

———◆———

Q. What is the largest natural lake in California?

A. Clear Lake.

———◆———

Q. Where in California is the largest wind-driven power plant?

A. Altemont Pass Windfarms.

Q. What is the oldest known Giant Sequoia?

A. Grizzly Giant, at 2,800 years of age.

———◆———

Q. What California lake is created with treated water from Lake Tahoe?

A. Indian Creek Reservoir.

———◆———

Q. What animals were used in the Sierras as pack animals in the 1860s?

A. Camels.

———◆———

Q. How tall is the Transamerica Pyramid in San Francisco?

A. 853 feet.

———◆———

Q. To where does the Monarch butterfly migrate each year?

A. Pacific Grove.

———◆———

Q. What area is called the "Salad Bowl of the World"?

A. Salinas Valley.

———◆———

Q. What was the oldest, richest, and most productive mine in North America?

A. The New Almaden Quicksilver (mercury) Mine in New Almaden.

Q. What town is home of the Broccoli Festival?

A. Greenfield.

———◆———

Q. Lake San Antonio is one of the largest winter habitats for what bird?

A. Bald Eagle.

———◆———

Q. More grapes are grown in what California county than anywhere else in the U.S.?

A. Monterey County.

———◆———

Q. What park is the site of the oldest, richest hardrock gold mine in California?

A. Empire Mine State Historic Park.

———◆———

Q. Where was the first successful steam-powered quartz gold mill?

A. Grass Valley.

———◆———

Q. California's first Bartlett pears were grown where?

A. Fruitvale district in Oakland.

———◆———

Q. When was the world's first regularly-transmitting radio station established in San Jose?

A. 1909.

Q. What is the name of the only salt-water lake wholly contained within an American city?

A. Lake Merritt, in Oakland.

Q. What city was once dubbed the "Egg Basket of the World"?

A. Petaluma.

Q. Who founded the Sierra Club?

A. John Muir.

Q. What is the Tehama-Colusa Fish Facility?

A. A man-made salmon-spawning channel.

Q. When was the last time Lassen Peak Volcano erupted?

A. 1917.

Q. What is California's largest migratory herd?

A. The Tehama deer herd.

Q. Where is the world's largest wind tunnel?

A. NASA-Ames Research Center, Moffett Field Naval Station.

Q. What construction project begun in 1938 required 4,000 men to finish?

A. Shasta Dam.

◆

Q. What is the largest underground stream in the U.S.?

A. The Salinas River.

◆

Q. What California city is called the "Camellia Capital of the World"?

A. Sacramento.

◆

Q. Where is the Southern Pacific Railroad's largest switching yard west of the Mississippi River?

A. Roseville.

◆

Q. How many hairpin turns make up Lombard Street in San Francisco?

A. Nine.

◆

Q. How high is Mount Shasta?

A. 14,162 feet.

◆

Q. What is the world's most beautiful suspension bridge?

A. Golden Gate Bridge.

Q. What are Seal Rocks?

A. Small, stony islands.

———◆———

Q. How many species are represented at the Monterey Bay Aquarium?

A. 600.

———◆———

Q. Where are the largest pumpkins in the West grown?

A. Acres of Pumpkins, Half Moon Bay.

———◆———

Q. Where can a U.S. Army Corps of Engineers' 1½-acre hydraulic working scale model of San Francisco Bay be seen?

A. San Francisco Bay Delta Model, Sausalito.

———◆———

Q. Where is the oldest grapevine in California?

A. Mission Santa Clara de Asis.

———◆———

Q. Where is the pioneer town for canned applesauce?

A. Sebastopol.

———◆———

Q. What is the oldest building in Golden Gate Park?

A. Conservatory of Flowers.

Q. Where is the "Almond Capital of the World"?

A. Ripon.

———◆———

Q. Where can bubbling mudpots, sulphur springs, and fumaroles be seen?

A. Lassen Volcanic National Park.

———◆———

Q. What world-famous mineral springs has the second-highest mineral content in the world?

A. Deerlick Springs.

———◆———

Q. Where did the world's largest hydraulic mine once operate?

A. Junction City.

———◆———

Q. Who was called the "Father of Irrigation in the Sacramento Valley"?

A. Will S. Green.

———◆———

Q. What was California's first state redwood park?

A. Big Basin Redwoods State Park.

———◆———

Q. What Monterey Bay town holds an annual Begonia Festival?

A. Capitola.

Q. Where was the world's first studio for receiving radio broadcasts?

A. Fairmont Hotel.

Q. Where are the World Championship Crab Races held each year?

A. Crescent City.

Q. Where was the largest gold nugget ever found in the U.S. discovered?

A. The Morgan Mine, 1854 (195 pounds).

Q. What park is famous for its towering granite crags?

A. Castle Crags State Park, Dunsmuir.

Q. What county produces more turkeys than any other place in the U.S.?

A. Fresno.

Q. What is the tallest artificial falls in the West?

A. Huntington Falls.

Q. What invention perfected in Petaluma enhanced the poultry industry?

A. The incubator.

Q. How old is Mono Lake?

A. Over 700,000 years.

———◆———

Q. Where was the French prune developed?

A. Santa Clara Valley.

———◆———

Q. What area is the leader in the American table wine industry?

A. Napa Valley.

———◆———

Q. What county has yielded more than half of California's total production of gold?

A. Nevada County.

———◆———

Q. When is the "rainy" season in California?

A. October to May.

———◆———

Q. What does the Feather River Hatchery produce?

A. Salmon and steelhead yearlings (more than 10 million annually).

———◆———

Q. Who created the Shasta daisy?

A. Luther Burbank.

Q. What Monterey Peninsula lighthouse has been continuously operational since 1855?

A. Point Pines Lighthouse.

Q. What area is referred to as the "Everglades of the West"?

A. Sacramento Delta.

Q. Which town claims the largest cork oak tree in California?

A. Campo Seco.

Q. Where are the world's highest bridge towers?

A. Golden Gate Bridge (746 feet).

Q. Who was the Scottish landscape gardener who transformed Golden Gate Park from wasteland to oasis?

A. John McLaren.

Q. Where is the Church of One Tree, built from a single redwood?

A. Santa Rosa.

Q. What Silverado area is noted for its hummingbirds?

A. Tucker Wildlife Sanctuary.

Q. How many computer-related manufacturers call the Silicon Valley (Sunnyvale area) home?

A. Over 670.

———◆———

Q. What is known as the world's smallest mountain range?

A. Sutter Buttes.

———◆———

Q. In what year was Yosemite National Park established?

A. 1890.

———◆———

Q. What is the California state flower?

A. Golden poppy.

———◆———

Q. What is the highest waterfall in North America?

A. Yosemite Falls.

———◆———

Q. What portion of California's land area is reserved for recreational use?

A. 25 percent.

———◆———

Q. When was the first telegraph installed in California?

A. 1861.

Q. Roughly, what is the value of the gold that has been found in California?

A. $2,000,000,000.

———◆———

Q. What lake at an altitude of 6,225 feet sits astride the California-Nevada border?

A. Lake Tahoe.

———◆———

Q. Who designed the Golden Gate Bridge?

A. Joseph Strauss.

———◆———

Q. How many acres of irrigated farmland are in California?

A. Over 8,000,000.

———◆———

Q. What size was Robert Kirkpatrick's world-record elephant garlic grown in Eureka in 1985?

A. 18½ inches in circumference (weighing 2 pounds, 12 ounces).

———◆———

Q. What is the California state tree?

A. California redwood.

———◆———

Q. Where is the Old Faithful Geyser of California?

A. Calistoga.

Q. What is California's largest river?

A. The Sacramento.

———◆———

Q. Where is the best place on land to view the gray whale migration?

A. Point Reyes Lighthouse.

———◆———

Q. From San Francisco to Monterey, what is the difference in the average daily temperature from summer to winter?

A. Ten degrees.

———◆———

Q. Where were the first dinosaur remains on the West Coast found?

A. Patterson.

———◆———

Q. What is chaparral?

A. Pygmy forests of shrubs, stunted trees, and plants.

———◆———

Q. What is the largest flying bird in the northern hemisphere?

A. California condor.

———◆———

Q. When was the position of conservation commissioner first created in California?

A. 1911.

Q. What is the California state bird?

A. California Valley quail.

———◆———

Q. What 60-year-old financier defended himself against a paternity suit on the grounds that the 31-year-old mother "was old and ugly"?

A. Lucky Baldwin.

———◆———

Q. When were oranges first introduced to California?

A. 1770.

———◆———

Q. How many gallons of paint are applied annually to the Golden Gate Bridge?

A. 5,000.

———◆———

Q. Where was the Magnavox loudspeaker developed?

A. Oakland.

———◆———

Q. What company is the largest raisin packer in the world?

A. Sun-Maid Raisins.

———◆———

Q. Who founded the Lick Observatory?

A. James Lick.

Q. What were Bodega Reds?

A. Potatoes (named for their bright maroon skins).

———◆———

Q. How did the Sequoia trees get their name?

A. For the Cherokee Indian chief, Sequoyah.

———◆———

Q. Where did Luther Burbank conduct his experiments in plant breeding?

A. Santa Rosa Valley.

———◆———

Q. Who was called the "Father of California Winemaking"?

A. Hungarian nobleman Col. Agaston Haraszthy.

———◆———

Q. Who brought the first smallpox vaccine to California?

A. James Ohio Pattie.

———◆———

Q. What dirigible formerly housed at Moffett Field crashed and burned?

A. The *Macon*.

———◆———

Q. Who was called the "Padre of the Rains" for his accurate weather forecasts?

A. Father Ricard.

Q. Where is James Lick buried?

A. Under one of the pillars supporting the telescope at the Lick Observatory.

———◆———

Q. Who built the first Kentucky log blockhouse in California?

A. George C. Yount.

———◆———

Q. Who was the leading grain farmer in the U.S. from 1874 until his death in 1883?

A. Dr. Hugh J. Glenn.

———◆———

Q. Who is reputed to have designed a covered bridge during his stay in Knight's Ferry?

A. Ulysses S. Grant.

———◆———

Q. What place advertised itself as the "World's Largest Peach, Apricot, and Nectarine Orchard"?

A. Tagus Ranch.

———◆———

Q. What was the weight of the largest gold nugget discovered at the Monumental Mine?

A. 100 pounds.

———◆———

Q. Who invented the water wheel in 1878 that led to the development of hydroelectric power?

A. Lester A. Pelton (of Comptonville).

Q. What was the weight of the largest gold bar ever produced in North Bloomfield?

A. 500 pounds.

Q. Who first discovered gold-bearing quartz in California?

A. George Knight, 1850.

Q. What made up the 25-acre "Persian prayer rug" at the Golden Gate International Exposition?

A. 1,500,000 cuttings of ice plant.

Q. How long did it take the Yankee Clipper, Flying Cloud, to travel from New York to San Francisco?

A. 81 days, 21 hours.

Q. How many varieties of grapes were imported from Europe to begin California's vineyards?

A. 1,400.

Q. What is the California state fish?

A. California golden trout.

Q. Who established the Clinic of Electronic Medicine in San Francisco?

A. Dr. Albert Abrams.

Q. What famed photographer once spent several summers as custodian of the Sierra Club lodge in Yosemite?

A. Ansel Adams.

◆

Q. Who won a 1968 Nobel Prize for his research on sub-atomic particles?

A. Luis Alvarez.

◆

Q. What family helped build the Pacific Gas and Electric pipeline, Hoover Dam, and the San Francisco Bay Bridge?

A. The Bechtel family.

◆

Q. Where was electricity first sent a distance of more than five miles?

A. From the Folsom Powerhouse to Sacramento (1895).

◆

Q. What formed the Devil's Postpile National Monument?

A. Basalt lava.

◆

Q. How did Rainbow Falls get its name?

A. From the rainbows that bounce off the falls at noon.

◆

Q. What race uses people-powered vehicles?

A. Cross-County Kinetic Sculpture Race.

Q. What California town celebrates with a Rhododendron Festival?

A. Eureka.

Q. Where is the Jughandle Ecological Staircase, a climb from level to a pygmy forest?

A. Near Fort Bragg.

Q. Where are the five-acre Forestiere Underground Gardens?

A. Fresno.

Q. What is the southernmost glacier in the U.S.?

A. Palisades Glacier.

Q. How old is the Bristlecone pine forest?

A. 4,600 years.

Q. Where is the largest orchid and gardenia nursery in the world?

A. Acres of Orchids, San Francisco.

Q. How much saltier is Mono Lake than the ocean?

A. Three times.

Q. How long is the San Francisco-Golden Gate bridge?

A. 8¼ miles

———◆———

Q. Where is the Butterfly Parade held to welcome the Monarchs?

A. Pacific Grove.

———◆———

Q. How many species of animals are in the San Francisco zoo?

A. Over 1,000.

———◆———

Q. At what university was the first cyclotron built?

A. University of California, Berkeley.

———◆———

Q. Where is the Luther Burbank Rose Festival held?

A. Santa Rosa.

———◆———

Q. Where is the only subjects-classified patent information stored other than in Washington, D.C.?

A. Sunnyvale Patents Information Clearinghouse.

———◆———

Q. What San Franciscan heiress became one of the world's greatest arctic explorers?

A. Louise Arner Boyd.

SCIENCE & NATURE

Q. Who was the first Nobel Prize winner from the University of California, Berkeley?

A. Ernest Orlando Lawrence.

———◆———

Q. Where did Edward Teller create the first thermonuclear device?

A. Livermore.

———◆———

Q. Who was called the "prophet of LSD"?

A. Dr. Timothy Leary.

———◆———

Q. What Sierra Club founder died in camp at Glacier Point?

A. Joseph LeConte.

———◆———

Q. What Stanford graduate built the first one-man chainsaw?

A. Robert Paxton McCulloch.

———◆———

Q. What University of California, Berkeley, professor led the Manhattan project?

A. J. Robert Oppenheimer.

———◆———

Q. What Big Sur resident has been called the "Father of Gestalt Therapy"?

A. Fritz Perls.

Q. What Stanford University graduate and "Star Trek" fan devised a scale for measuring earthquake intensity?

A. Charles Francis Richter.

Q. Where is the Rellim Demonstration Forest?

A. Crescent City.

Q. What state reserve is known for its large colony of northern elephant seals?

A. Ano Nuevo State Reserve.

Q. Where can one monitor fish ladders?

A. Salmon Viewing Plaza, Red Bluff.

Q. Where can Blue Diamond Almond Groves be toured?

A. Sacramento.

Q. Where is the famed Morgan Horse Ranch that supplies park rangers' horses?

A. Point Reyes.

Q. Who discovered Mount Shasta in 1827?

A. Peter Skene Ogden.

Q. Where was the first steam gristmill built?

A. Bodega.

———◆———

Q. In 1852 what San Francisco-based lumberman established the first sawmill at Mendocino?

A. Alderman Harry Meiggs.

———◆———

Q. Where are the Sebastiani Vineyards and Wineries?

A. Sonoma.

———◆———

Q. What San Jose park is known as "Little Yosemite"?

A. Alum Rock Park.

———◆———

Q. Where is the Lick Observatory?

A. At Mount Hamilton.

———◆———

Q. What is the unique feature of San Juan Bautista?

A. The San Andreas Fault intersects the town.

———◆———

Q. What was once the home of the world's largest apple orchard?

A. Novato.

Q. What is the highest point on the Monterey Peninsula?
A. Jacks Peak (1,068 feet).

———◆———

Q. Where are the Sterling Vineyards?
A. Calistoga.

———◆———

Q. What natural barrier is between California and Oregon?
A. The Siskiyou Mountains.

———◆———

Q. Where is the home of the world's richest, deepest gold mines?
A. Jackson.

———◆———

Q. What area offers a 360-degree panoramic view of San Francisco?
A. Twin Peaks.

———◆———

Q. What town is home to the Robert Mondavi Winery?
A. Oakville.

———◆———

Q. How did the town of Confidence get its name?
A. From the Confidence Mine, which justified its name by producing $4.25 million in gold.

Q. Where were the "lost cement mines" that were supposedly filled with gold in the cement veins?

A. Monoville on the shore of Mono Lake.

---◆---

Q. What is the second largest natural lake in California?

A. Eagle Lake, in Lassen County.

---◆---

Q. Where is Humboldt Lagoons State Park?

A. Orick.

---◆---

Q. What is the elevation of the Devil's Postpile Monument?

A. 7,600 feet.

---◆---

Q. Where is the Chateau Souverain Winery?

A. Geyserville.

---◆---

Q. Siskiyou County is home to what famous mountain?

A. Mount Shasta.

---◆---

Q. Where is California's Petrified Forest?

A. Between Santa Rosa and Calistoga.

Q. What community was named for the blue wildflowers on its hillsides?

A. Larkspur.

———◆———

Q. Where are the Monterey Vineyards?

A. Gonzales.

———◆———

Q. Where was the first mill for crushing quartz built?

A. Grass Valley.

———◆———

Q. Where is the world's "raisin center"?

A. Fresno.

———◆———

Q. What is the Turntable?

A. Where San Francisco's cable cars are manually turned around.

———◆———

Q. Where are the Piper Sonoma Cellars and White Oak Vineyards?

A. Healdsburg.

———◆———

Q. What mountain summit was chosen in 1851 as the base point for all U.S. surveys in California?

A. Mount Diablo.

Q. Where in San Francisco can an authentic Oriental garden be found?

A. Japanese Tea Garden.

---◆---

Q. Where was the first great sugar beet refinery built?

A. Near Watsonville.

---◆---

Q. Grass Valley is home to what fabulous gold mine?

A. Empire Mine.

---◆---

Q. Where was the commerical process for pickling ripe olives developed?

A. Oroville.

---◆---

Q. Where is Ano Nuevo State Reserve?

A. Pescadero.

---◆---

Q. Where is the Kruse Rhododendron State Reserve?

A. Plantation.

---◆---

Q. What did Robert Louis Stevenson call the "Mont Blanc of the Coast Range"?

A. Mount St. Helena.

Q. Where is the Eldorado National Forest?

A. Placerville.

———◆———

Q. Where is the Easter in July Lily Festival held?

A. Crescent City.

———◆———

Q. What area surrounds the Devil's Postpile National Monument?

A. Inyo National Forest.

———◆———

Q. Where is the Korbel Winery?

A. Guerneville.

———◆———

Q. What city produces twenty percent of the world's almonds?

A. Chico.

———◆———

Q. What town billed itself as "Home of the Merced Sweet Potato"?

A. Atwater.

———◆———

Q. Chester is the home of what large sawmill?

A. Collins Pine Sawmill.

Q. What are the Minarets?

A. Jagged, unique peaks in the Sierra Nevada Mountains.

———◆———

Q. Where is the Sunol Regional Wilderness?

A. Livermore.

———◆———

Q. Where is the Lassen National Forest?

A. Burney.

———◆———

Q. Where is the Black Diamond Mines Regional Preserve?

A. Antioch.

———◆———

Q. Where do 97 percent of the world's sequoias grow?

A. Along US-101 for 387 miles (known as the Redwood Highway).

———◆———

Q. What winery is situated in Middletown?

A. The Guenoc Winery.

———◆———

Q. Where is the Modoc National Wildlife Refuge?

A. Alturas.